HISTORY OF THEATRE

OR

THE GLASS OF FASHION

M. G. Stephens

MADHAT PRESS
CHESHIRE, MASSACHUSETTS

MadHat Press
MadHat Incorporated
PO Box 422, Cheshire, MA 01225

The Library of Congress has assigned
this edition a Control Number of
2020947643

ISBN 978-1-952335-13-6 (paperback)

Text by M. G. Stephens
Author photograph by S. E. Wolan
Cover design by Marc Vincenz
Cover image: *Cubist Self-Portrait* by Salvador Dalí, 1923.

www.madhat-press.com

First Printing

for Susan, a Chicago blossom,
for your love and understanding, *sempre*

Table of Contents

Part Three

PART FOUR

Part Five

"Who's there?"

PART ONE

Part One

Ham Omelet

O'Shaughnessy sat in his favorite greasy spoon on upper Broadway, eating the breakfast special of a ham omelet with yellow rice and black beans. He was struck by the thought that he was about to play Hamlet. But not just any Hamlet. His Prince was ten weeks in the making, eight in rehearsals, two in previews. His Hamlet was an historical one, back in the beginnings of drama, a subject Cornelius Michael O'Shaughnessy—some called him Michael or Mike or even Mick, while others called him Con or Connie or (the ones who did not like him very much) that con artist Michael O'Shaughnessy—had not pondered since his undergraduate days as a theatre major. Back then, he had been required to take the history of theatre course in order to graduate. As he sipped strong Spanish coffee, he saw the chorus come through the *paradoi,* and he thought, I was still in the scene house, awaiting my grand entrance. After the great triumvirate of Aeschylus, Sophocles, and Euripides died, and the Greeks fell out of power, I began to take more liberties with my lines, Mr. O'Shaughnessy thought. Then the emperor Lycurgus passed an edict which forbade the actor from doing this, and it was then I decided to leave Athens and to venture back to Sicily. There were great things still happening abroad, now that Titus Andronicus had assumed the stage, and I went back to working in mimes, and also found myself portraying the Greek characters, albeit for the Romans now. Menander sought me out for his comedies, and I was working often in his plays, mixing the stories, getting some laughs, living a good life for one who was almost now a slave. But the other actors were talking about Rome, and so I thought I must make my fortune there and went northward with the caravan, stopping in the Atellan for some farces and mime work along the way.

On Up to Beyond

Here is frivolous conjecture: I am alive again, azaleas. It is spring and I am dry, feeling quite neat about it. I am alive again, though I was never really dead or not alive, it is more like one come back to his own skin, not a new man, I am my old self again, yet different entirely from the moments which preceded me here. Crab apple, cherry blossom, dogwood, they burst for the first time this season, and like that, an old strategy lumbers inside my chest, of me and that I am. What it is, I'm on, I'm hot, I take off my coat, I roll up my sleeves, I walk.

THE ACADEMY

She wore her straw hat and an antique flower-print dress that flowed to mid-calf. Under the yellow and white tent in the garden, she drank cherry-pink punch, rum-spiked, and smiled. The day was hot and muggy, and night proved no different, and she worried about getting to the ballet by eight o'clock. All of this was so long ago, I shouldn't remember any of it, and yet just the other day I thought of that rundown neighborhood where the academy was located, and immediately I saw her again: straw hat, antique flower print dress, pale and blonde, slightly intoxicated, and anxious to get to the ballet. The thought of her has taken me away from learning my lines.

THE SNOWY OWL

Ophelia said: we know
What we are,
But know not what
We may be.

She said: they say the owl
Was a baker's daughter.
I have a friend
Who was just that.

The Bishop's Lawn

After the dog days of Morningside, the neighborhood still empty like a college town, even though this is New York City and V & T pizza is half-filled with hospital workers from St. Luke's and the Hungarian pastry shop has only a handful of graduate students reading the Saturday paper and books by Foucault and Roland Barthes, we go to the gardens next to St. John the Divine, the property ripped and torn with construction on a peace fountain—God bless them—and the plot where we raised a child daily, taught her to name things and make speeches from the stone pulpit while the peacocks hooted and the male birds spread their colorful wings, and where she tossed paper airplanes from impossible heights, the plot is now cordoned off and we go rearward to another lawn, you with your busted fibula and leg in a cast, myself the dutiful father carrying the plastic chess set under my arm, the beginners, moving pawns and rooks and queen too soon until a security guard shouts to get the hell off the lawn, though there is no sign and we have taken to it a thousand times with the peacocks and rooster, pigeons and ants, and looking for answers, I see the bishop moving diagonally from his house, and I ask why I can't play chess on the lawn, my daughter with her cast and broken fibula, Oh, don't bother me, he shouts, waving his hands downward and disgusted, he's had enough talk with the merely mortal for one day—besides which, they're probably not even parishioners but riff-raff from the neighborhood—his face twisted with impatience and annoyance above the seersucker suit and the clerical collar. No one is allowed on the bishop's lawn, another security guard says, and so carrying her on my back, we walk to the Biblical garden in the rear of the property, just next to the Cathedral School, away from the precious ecumenical lawn, cock crow, peacock strut, shrunken Bible flowers bend in the mid-afternoon, Oh God, I pray, give your bishop manners and a sense of humor, let us finish our chess game in Your garden, the king is exposed, I lost my bishop, and who the hell does that goddamn son-of-a-bitch think he is talking to us like that? You see, God, we had been sitting on that lawn for years, raising a child here, well, not here, but down the block, and coming here every day in nice weather, which we thank You for, and suddenly that bishop appears like a figure in a chess game, moving diagonally in the direction of an economy-sized American car. Her ankle, I mean, her fibula is broken, not her ankle, but her fibula, and we can't move easily, and first the security guard (pawn), then the bishop (s.o.b.), then the next guard (another pawn) tell us to get off the lawn. The bishop exposed his King! The bishop exposed his King!

The Glass of Fashion (1)

About my face, what is it? Smile wrinkles, I don't show wear, vats of beer, truckloads of cigarettes, like Hamlet, I was the glass of fashion, presenting the social cast of an only child, how often I was mistaken for that, the wandering Jew, the charming Italian or Catholic or one of ten children, my father with whom I hardly saw eye to eye, even his face appears to me in the dirty mirror, my hand on the verge of lather and razor, I am 36 years old, I say, and I cannot remember the last time my ex-wife or another woman flirted with this face, yet inside and behind it, I am at least half those years, I hope, I wait, I shave and go outside, searching for Polonius.

Get off the Stage

The theatre was so crowded that the usher asked if I would not mind sitting on the apron of the stage. A folding chair had been placed there, in front of a desk which was part of the stage furniture. It was a two-character play, a male and female actor. The conflict was a domestic one, for his wife had discovered that her husband had a girlfriend. The wife was dressed plainly, cotton dress, simple shoes, her hair tied with a bandana, while her husband had on an expensive black suit, an expensive white shirt and tie, and wore much gold jewelry. The female character makes a good deal of reference to his dress, because he works in a factory, and does not need to dress like this. He says that he wears the suit after work for business reasons; he is trying to advance his career. I am simultaneously wrapped into the fabric of the plot and at once bored and tired. When I am not right with them, leaning forward in the folding chair, my elbows propped on the desk top, I am nodding off, unable to focus on their activity. Occasionally someone in the audience startles me awake by yelling for me to move my head or chair or to get off the stage, because I am in their sightline. The usher explains to the vociferous audience member that I paid for my seat just like he did, and that if he has any problem, please see the house manager after the show or at the intermission. When I nod off, I can see that the male actor is displeased, but his female counterpart appears oblivious to me except when I am attentive to her lines, her movements, her stage business. Once she breaks her focus and concentration, comes out of character, and winks at me. The male actor once gave me a dirty look after I came to, startled, after nodding off; he broke his concentration and frowned at me, right in the middle of a tender moment with his leading lady. "I like this play, don't get me wrong," I whisper, and his reply, sitting at the chair behind the desk, is a quiet "shut up," until he comes back into the action with his wife. When the intermission comes, one and one-half hours later, I carefully move to the lobby, and then leave the theatre for home, once I realize that I am really Hamlet and have my own theatrical space to inhabit, and not this contemporary one where I didn't belong....

THIS AIN'T NO OPHELIA, HONEY

This weary night I lay down to sleep and dream, my mouth stale from drink and garlic, the dimensions of my room flat and black, the status of my feelings unprofitable. At first I thought it seemed this way—*seemed.* I asked myself—not, it *is,* but *seems?* For many hours I lay awake, unable to sleep, but finally I drifted off, my breath iambic and even, no longer rushed and full of the fever of the day, I rested. I dreamed, too. What I dreamed was not of Ophelia, though I thought of her before sleep, as I did my mother, thinking of them in one image. This night was given to Helen, I do not know why, but it was of her I dreamt, as though she were everywhere, and nowhere at all. I had been thinking of an anecdote about James Joyce in which he named an ugly photograph of a woman after Helen. A man, Schwarz by name, accused Joyce of killing Helen when the writer pointed out how old she must be after living with Menelaus, then Paris, her time in Troy, and then how old she was when Dante saw her in the Inferno. "Killed Helen," Joyce said, laughing. Yet the Helen I saw was even older than Joyce's; she was before goat song and the dithyramb. I walked in this dream past Thespis, then Arion, back into the drama, into the pre-history, into her moment. There I stood in her bedroom in Troy. Like a casting director I had in my hand her résumé and photos. I am Hamlet, I told her. You little weasel, she said, have you ever been fucked? she asked. I mean have you ever really been fucked good, my little man in your britches and buskins? Well, I said, there's always Ophelia, and she laughed, Helen let out this awful guffaw. Get over here, she smirked, Prince of Denmark.

Sullen Flesh

From the rehearsal loft on the West Side, midtown, I went out into the traffic, the noise of the city, the murders and muggings, the betrayals, the highs. At thirty-six, smoking too much, drinking, but always active, I am preparing myself for the part of my life. I am to play Hamlet. It seems as though all my life has led up to this moment, and maybe everything else will lead away from it. I think of a remark which the Shakespeare scholar Jan Kott made about Hamlet being a sponge. I am a sponge. I am the sponge. This week I am to borrow money to pay my rent from one friend; then borrow more from an old girlfriend—to buy some food and do laundry. I've stopped driving my taxi to prepare for Hamlet, the sponge. This is my big moment. The great Polish director Andrei Krakau will direct me. Other Poles are involved, too, as it should be, because when I think about Hamlet, I do not think about Denmark or England, but rather, like Pere Ubu, I think of Poland. Mirkowicz is the dramaturg. There is Sonia, the dressmaker, doing costumes; she has no last name. Sets are minimal, but lighting is crucial, and will be done by Jan Lapchik. Ophelia is being played by Olga Lublin; Claudius by Jan Warsawa. The rest of the cast is made of lesser known and unknown Poles and Americans, all of them studying with Andrei at his Zloty Theatre Lab. All of this proves to be very important for me since I think this is to be a great production, though all of us have already anticipated the critics out to get us. Paranoia? No, I have been around too long. Already I have a belly sprouting, too much beer after rehearsals with Andrei and the others. Now I must go home to my studio apartment for rest; I live uptown, not a good neighborhood, not safe, not fashionable, but the rent is cheap, all my books are there, I call it home....

HAMLET'S DREAM

I am Hamlet, yet I am not, etc. I feel like the Dane; I think like the Prince; I look like him, people have said. Why else would they give me the part? And yet, and yet, and yet. I am a player; I am prepared to *play* Hamlet, not really *be* Hamlet. Don't you nincompoops understand my dilemma? I put on my make-up. Before the make-up I am me, who is also Hamlet, though maybe others will not think that I am when I walk down the street. But they are idiots! They are without talent and brains like I am. I put on my make-up and step into my costume. It is contemporary dress for this version of the play, and yet a costume is a costume, and thus it allows me to assume my part. I will not wear any black turtleneck, but only the right one for the part, the turtleneck that shouts out that it, like me, is Hamlet. Like the jeans. These must be jeans that call out Hamlet. But then Andrei made a change in the costumes. Now I wear a rugby shirt, less bright, but my collar is white; I wear glasses occasionally. My trousers are of a king's thread—*corde du roi,* a thick nap corduroy, burgundy colored. My shoes are Nikes. You fools will never understand, but let me explain to you that this is the ultimate Hamlet I am about to play, and so what I have given you is the ultimate apparel for a thirty-three-year-old graduate student of philosophy, a man obsessed, would you not agree, with deconstructionist views, a man who has read Walter Benjamin, who knows Nietzsche and Hegel backwards and forwards, for all of this is Hamlet, too. And now do you understand why Andrei has made Hamlet dress this way?

The Bus Driver on Madison Avenue

I hate 57th and Madison because when I am there—I mean I am here now—that means that I have been to the periodontist which is my adult version of the childhood orthodontist, a mouth and teeth and gum and root person, come to wreak havoc—or is it wreck havoc?—on my mouth, all the time dreaming of new wings on her house in Nassau County, fishing boats in Port Jefferson, or sending her children to Ivy League colleges, all thanks to my bad teeth and gums. "I don't understand," a Chinese dentist I used to go to once said, examining yet another gum problem. "This only happens to Irish people and alcoholics. Why is it happening to you?" And, yet, a paddy boy, a son of Danny Boy, an alkie in recovery, I had to laugh at his observation, like saying to Miles Davis, Ralph Ellison, James Baldwin, or Thelonious Monk, "I don't understand why this is happening to you, sir, because it only happens to black people." So there I was on 57th Street at Madison Avenue, my mouth sore and ripped apart, waiting for the Number Four bus to transport me uptown, crosstown, and home, but matters were slowed by a German tourist in front of me, without change, only dollar bills, the driver told him, "Ask someone for change, 'cause I sure as hell don't got it," and when the tourist came back empty-handed, the driver, firm but friendly, told him not to be shy, "Go ahead, ask," he said, "these are New Yorkers, the friendliest, nicest people in the world," and the bus of New Yorkers let out with applause, as if the driver had just sung a great operatic aria. They clapped. And one of them gave the man four quarters for his dollar bill, and I forgot about my gums and teeth and human misery for fifty-three blocks uptown and the mile or so it took to cross from east side to west, riding with the friendliest, nicest people

in the world, through Harlem, the most beautiful place in the
city, where great herons, even night herons and blue herons
perched, one-legged in the Harlem Meer.

All of this for a mere buck
and several more bits, my mouth
Novocain numb,
and the sunshine poking through
the low gray clouds.

PHILOSOPHICAL INVESTIGATIONS

Elizabethans ate too much bread and drank too much ale, and so I do the same, because Hamlet is of his time, and his time was that of Shakespeare. Yes, I am off the wagon. I have stopped going to AA meetings. I have taken back my will. After eating and drinking too much, he walks around, carrying a book. This evening I have chosen Wittgenstein's *Philosophical Investigations,* but it is only for tonight. Sometimes I carry Derrida or Barthes, Foucault or Braudel. It has not escaped him, though perhaps it has everyone else including Andrei the Director, that Hamlet's tastes in literature lean toward the French. This is important, too, because what book he chooses affects him on stage, deep inside his character, to know which book he is reading, which one influences him, his decisions, his choices. That is Hamlet's dilemma. What to choose? And failing that, then being still, finding an inability to act, though not to think or feel; Hamlet is the type of character who cannot stop thinking or feeling, and sometimes he mistakes one for the other, though this is not his tragic flaw. This is O'Shaughnessy's dilemma.

THE TRAGIC RHYTHM

Let me say immediately that I have no problem in acting upon the tragic rhythm; it is a movement that I am comfortable with. I think it goes back to my roots in Catholicism, an inevitability, the ineluctable modality if you will. (I must try to figure out why James Joyce keeps reappearing every time I think of Hamlet.) Yes, I act; but I also do. I am, therefore I act. I act therefore I do. I do therefore I am. Therefore, I act, I am, I do. Yet how many of us can claim to have murdered their lover's father? To think is to do; to do is to think. To act is to think; to think is to act. Doo-bee-doo-bee-doo ...

Prism, Mirror, Labyrinth

If I am Hamlet, then I go to sleep as Hamlet and wake up as Hamlet, and I do, I am, I act, I think, therefore I get up and brush my teeth and go out to work. I am Hamlet. And yet I am not Hamlet. I am also myself. Sometimes this becomes a problem. But then again sometimes there is no problem at all. I am what I am. (Popeye) And that's all I am. (Oh, Popeye, says Olive Oyl.) There is a point in every day, though, whether I am Hamlet or not, when I become Hamlet—I really am the Prince of Denmark, my home in Elsinore. It may last for three hours; in its original it might last six or seven hours. That does not depend upon my moods but the needs of the company, especially the director, in this case Andrei, who cuts and pastes, changes things around, more often than not cutting out Fortinbras, even once cutting the gravediggers, as I remember—what a dire deletion! But even if I am Hamlet, and I am Hamlet, I can only be Hamlet after certain lines have been cut, more often than not. Ideally I am three to three and a half hours long. I have been many things—I should say that Hamlet has been many things—I have only been one Hamlet and one Hamlet only—it is those other Hamlets, some of them impostors, some more Hamlet than I. They can out-Hamlet Hamlet. But what is Hamlet to me or I to Hamlet? First, I am bounded. Understand that I am not infinite, although I have been played with infinite variation. No matter who is Hamlet or how he, or even she, creates him, he inhabits a space, and that space is a universe. Is space opened or closed? With Hamlet it is closed, finite, bounded. (All of this should give you some clue already about him.) I have my three boards and a passion.

The Business of Hamlet

There is a thrust; there is a rake. I come forward; often I am coming at you. My interiors seem to be more for those outside my universe, this stage. I project them outward, breaking through the limits of my own space, cutting across the warp of time and space, into you. You. You are sitting in your chair, in your booth, or even one of the groundlings responds. I tell them who I am, Hamlet, Prince of Denmark. Then I act upon that information. I am not Oedipus; I am not Godot. But all characters may find parts of themselves in me. All people may find a part of themselves or even all of themselves in Hamlet. That is how I became Hamlet, for I was not Hamlet once upon a time. Then I saw another Hamlet and I thought—this is better than a convention of Elvis imitators—I could be more Hamlet than this Hamlet. This Hamlet is not even Hamlet. I am not sure if I was always Hamlet, though, but that he was submerged within me, or whether I was not Hamlet at all until I saw another Hamlet trying to be Hamlet. Once I was not Hamlet; now I am Hamlet in all my bones, in all my speech, in my blocking, my gestures, my business. I must first entertain you with that idea that I am Hamlet; but shortly after that I must move you to believe that I am Hamlet; finally I will change you so that you never thought otherwise. He is Hamlet all right, you will say. There never was a Hamlet until he was Hamlet. The illusion of the first time. Hamlet is as Hamlet does.

After a Reading by Milosz

This morning I woke in fog, the sun shining, but my bearings were cockeyed. Yesterday I'd worked too much, not on what I want and like to do, say revising my book, but teaching, four hours in the Bronx, nonstop, then several more hours in the evening at Columbia. When I walked off the campus, it was mizzling rain, and a few beers didn't cut me down a few notches, only told me I was real tired, but I wasn't going to sleep for a long time. I watched Ted Koppel interview Ferdinand Marcos, then drifted through David Letterman, phasing out into the morning hours, a movie, the news, I can't remember now. My daughter, I heard, in the kitchen, discussing why she hated Bloody Marys and Old Fashioneds, probably dressed in her school blouse already, though I wouldn't know, still laid out in my bed. I'm usually the one up to make breakfast. Her six-year-old voice drifts through my head, things about her music teacher or her gym teacher, her enthusiasm for school tempered by them. Then there is this faint trace of Cole Porter, as though coming from another planet, and when I wake, the apartment is empty, the super still has not fixed the radiator, the day is long begun and nearly even over for others. It is my day to go to the gym, to get back to running, to jump rope, shadow-box, imagine myself as if I were fit, which I am not, the cigarettes, the back-to-drinking which New York induces, the big book on the table, waiting for me to rewrite it. I can't even call anyone; I'm not interested in conversation, in speech. I load my things in a bag to go to the gym, but chicken out and call home, asking my wife out for lunch, and we do it. Then I pick up my daughter at school, and she's real surprised to see me, expecting her mother. We have a soda, talk a lot, play in the playground, then take the bus back home. I start to read a play that my wife is supposed to audition for, but all I'm thinking about is her singing Cole Porter, and how I haven't heard the vibrancy of her voice in five or six years. She'd stopped singing opera, like that, period, and hadn't sung in that many years, then suddenly, the rooms are going crazy with Cole Porter, and I'm feeling like the top. I go downtown to hear Czeslav Milosz at the Donnell Library, and even forty-five minutes before the reading, there isn't a seat in the house. I've read one of his books, and am expecting this brilliant, dour, philosophical man to speak, and instead, when the room quiets, he is witty, full of life, even funny, and I'm thinking about Andrei or my friends in Poland, where I'm supposed to go in December—many zlotys await me because they're publishing my first novel—and I'm not feeling sad, I'm feeling real sensual, alive, really good, thinking of Cole Porter and afterward I go for drinks with Mark and Hugh, and we get talking in this uptown West Side bar, and I keep telling myself, this is great, this is better than Paris, this is better than Berlin, this is the top, this New York, and lines from "Love for Sale" or "From This Moment On" race through my head, and I ask the waiter for another Rolling Rock....

BEFORE SLEEP

Her name is Venus after a painting by Velasquez, the room a red chamber. The redness is of a blood passion, the boiling point of the senses. She reclines. There is the couch, the pillows, the poof. Her backside is offered as if a naked peach. I can taste her and smell her, though she is only there in my thoughts. She holds a mirror in her hand, and I see her face, the black hair, the high cheekbones, the curls and curves and circles. This is what I think about before sleep, and sometimes I do not find sleep for many hours.

Half-Ass and Me, Half-Drunk, at a Back Table in the Half Moon

If Henry Hudson stopped here, it was a night when sinks clogged and the river named after him rolled down Fordham Road in the Bronx. (Oh, them Fordham Indians, they do know how to paddle them there canoes across Spuyten Duyvil and other swirling eddies.) People come from miles away, including New Rochelle and Yonkers to eat their hearts out, burp garlic, and drink Italian wine in the places on Arthur Avenue, but this place is like a corner pizza parlor, only with a backroom with red-and-white-checked tablecloths, and a lady who sticks her head out of the heated kitchen. (Some days her face is like Anna Magnani; sometimes she looks beautiful, though deranged; somewhere I saw her on the street as ugly as your sister.) Hey, Half-Ass says, you want to step outside and fight me like a man, nobody says nothing bad about my sister! Take it easy, chill out, I said, or you'll die of massive seizures, especially after all that garlic bread and red wine, I don't even know your sister, Half-Ass. (This was a lie, 'cause his sister and me, we go on the fly to motels near Whitestone, and I even seen her pee into her own hand and blow the wiz into the air like bubbles.) Did you know that Henry Hudson's boat, the *Half Moon,* sailed up the Hudson River, ages ago, I asked Half-Ass, who ordered us another bottle of house red. Fuck you, he said, you big-mouth phony with your ideas and your, and your whatever you got, credit cards, which ain't worth shit here, go down the block to Amici's. (Half-Ass, I said. Don't call me that, he shouted, my name is Cornelius, just like yours, and you got no business telling me about some man's boat when I know for certain he drove a car, 'cause

24

there's a parkway named after him which you ought to get on and drive north out of my sight, ya bastard.) Everybody around here knows that the Half Moon has nothing to do with Henry Hudson and boats because it was named after the Full Moon Café which burnt to the ground many moons ago, and they opened this pizza joint and little bistro, only half the size of the old one. How I know this, Half-Ass, Cornelius that is, told me, and a man with a sister like his can't be all that dumb.

The Ex-Seaman

Hell-bent on raising hell, I raised a child from my thirtieth year outward, but I did not make good wages, my raises were poor, I scampered at the mouth of poverty, educated but lacking a sense of cut-throat dealings, back-bent, I raised potatoes, I drove a cab, I went fishing, and now two doors from Hell, I make this testament, a broken, busted bag of wind and air, I once was charming, and charmed mostly the ladies, but I ain't been laid in close to twenty-five years except if you count my fist, and still I am a child of God, this seventieth year to Heaven, I declare, fuck it all and drink a beer, let me out of here, I got the heebie-jeebies, and I ain't sure where I am or who I is, or even if that's grammatically speaking kosher and all right, so all right, it's night, and I'm sundowning, scared to death because I got wet brain, and come in and out of lucidity, oh Lucy, this is Ricky Ricardo, I been hijacked by a band of mariachis, help me.

THE DESIRES OF TOYS

Rebus doubts and illuminated signs of commerce all collect at the eyes' borders like mustaches on the immigration police in those strife years when strivers and old gang mentalities directed the collateral urges of the nouveau lumpen terminally circuited video cassette modular home chips and spools blindingly floated in wind tunnels of avenues of the old city. Honk honk. The imagination of the immigrant on a holiday of cornfed thighs and the eyes of hostesses alert to the nuances of a cultured overcoat or socks and their politics as though verticality were everything because it was everywhere. I write this on a towel in the steamroom of a commissary outside the desires of toys and governments because the light in my room blinks I think I will not jog or if I think too much that act might jog me silly how silly to begin and even more foolish to end. To a man they whisper amen while the women loom or spin threads and the wheels limp out another injustice of sounds without bread. Oh, look, I'm dead.

THE FOURTEENTH BLACKBIRD

It had been snowing, and it was snowing, then it stopped. Now it was about to snow again. Again, I looked out the high windows of the house. I had seen a man, and I was seeing him, I was about to see him again. His name was Wallace, and he wore a gray suit with a white shirt and an old thick tie probably from his alma mater. He was not a smoker of big cigars, and his breath steamed out, though I cannot say whether it was scented of bourbon or Scotch. About his head I saw blackbirds almost daily. Then in this tangle of winter's days and nights, I saw only one blackbird. Then he walked in the snow along with nothing, no birds, no words, just himself and his enormous thoughts inside his hatless head.

ENDEAVOUR

Out there, which is nowhere, the Earth behind them like a giant ball of blue-green cheese, they tether themselves to the mothership, hoping to snag the wayward satellite. Once the three astronauts floated in space, awaiting the errant satellite to latch onto, the danger of a spacesuit rip had to be forgotten. The 4.5-ton satellite was weightless, but still had mass. Meaning, it might knock the shit out of any one of them, might even careen into Endeavour, sending it spinning off into deep space forever malfunctioned. Any acceleration in the wrong direction, this orbiting hulk might swirl amok. More than four hours later, the astronauts maneuvered the satellite into the bay, the New York Rangers just defeated by the Pittsburgh Penguins in the Stanley Cup playoffs. Somewhere between sport and construction-worker bare-fisted know-how, they grasp the rotating communications cylinder, dumping it into the payload bay, another honest day's work achieved. Yet I could not help but marvel at them, 230 miles above our planet, these human yo-yos, these scientists and engineers, "Houston," Captain Daniel C. Brandenstein said, "I think we've got a satellite."

TRAGEDY

Knock-knock.
Who's there?
Hamlet.
Hamlet *who?*
Your dead father.

PART TWO

Movement Class

I have given up a lot to be an actor; I have forsaken a wife and family, dropped out of graduate school, spent a lot of money on acting classes in New York, whored myself after producers and casting directors, lived hand to mouth, scraping money together for voice lessons, movement classes, trips to Poland, to England, downtown to cold lofts, out of town to regional theatres, out to Hollywood for bit parts or almost landing big parts, sometimes getting talking roles. I've worked on the soaps; I've done commercials. I am thirty-six years old, six-feet-one-inch tall, one hundred and eighty pounds; I'm getting heavier each year. Once I was very trim. I read more than most actors; my apartment, one room, is filled with thousands of books: poetry, fiction, philosophy, Irish literature, Chinese and Japanese literature, books on dance, books on Matisse and Picasso, and, of course—mostly plays and the dramaturgy of it. My hair is dark brown, thinning, though I am not yet bald. My chest is 44 inches. I run, skip, jump rope, play paddleball in the park, or get in some squash or racquetball in the gym. Women have found me interesting; some have fallen madly in love with me. None of my relationships has lasted. Blame it on the profession. It isn't a coincidence that the whores work in Times Square. The whores work across the street from the Yale Rep in New Haven. They worked across from the Globe, from the Theatre of Athens, from the Sicilian stage. That's show business. The whores lived across from the palace at Elsinore. Perhaps that is the smell that Hamlet refers to. The smell of whores and theatre, the interbraided twosome, the twins. But soon I am to embark upon the part of my life. I am to play Hamlet, the Dane, the Prince of Denmark....

The Early-Rising Hamlet

I was born before history, but don't think that a vague remark. It was in the south of what you now call Italy. Some dispute the exact whereabouts, if it was in the Atellan or in Sicily, but I will tell you here that it was in the animal mimes in Sicily, where I wore a rabbit's foot on my belt, had a diamond-shaped pattern on my blouse, and instead of Polonius, Gertrude, and Claudius, there were Bucco, Macco, the others. We moved slowly in those days, and I was no different than anyone else. It would be some time before I went to Athens, for the Great Dionysia, for the festival, that is; the dithyramb, the agon, the tragic contests. Arion brought me with him; I remember that well. It was Arion. And instead of reciting, we introduced movements to the chorus. Oh, I was nothing special in those days, another chorister, another voice chanting the poems. But then it was many years later, and Thespis wanted more than that, and so he asked me to step forward to recite some lines about Hercules. Then it moved even further, until I was reciting lines from the House of Atreus, and finally I was playing Oedipus. (Hamlet playing Oedipus? she asks. Yes, is my answer.) I won my laurel wreath that year, because they recognized the protagonist as well as the playwright, and I had a good meal of garlic, lettuce and eels, along with wine. When I was not on stage, I taught the politicians how to speak. Or we were touring the countryside. There was always something to do; something to act. He who answers is often called hypocrite. Solon called me a dissembler, an artificer, one who dissimulates. But if you do not act you cannot be called a thespian. I was honored that they called me hypocrite. It was a great honor, indeed.

WHAT I LIKE

What I like are (not shoes like Imelda or gold like Midas baseball or teams like George or buildings Donald) books, clothes, a nice car. I'm not ready for a Cadillac Coupe de Ville, but give me a couple of years and I will be ready for a Caddy. What I'd like right now is something well-running yet not so slick on the outside that it draws attention to itself and makes the street guys want to slit my throat and drive off in the night with my Lexus or Acura or Infiniti, some dumb old dirty Honda would do me fine, even an old Dodge Dart as long as the engine ran well. As for the clothes, they have to be slick, not gangster, not dangerous, but the more expensive the better, the flashier is all right too, neat and sharp as a tack, creases in the pants that cut like sharp knives, no gold jewelry, thank you, no fancy chains, though I do like a nice watch, maybe one good ring, a barrel cane, I'd wear the hat on my head cocked to the side, a Borsalino, soft as a baby's butt, not bad, no, not bad, or even tough, but tough enough, as though I would not be worth the trouble to bother for a light, a dime, a walk around the block in the middle of the dark, I'd be cool, of course, my clothes real sharp, my car very smart, and my apartment filled with books, on the shelves, in the kitchen on those shelves, even in the refrigerator, and maybe some might overflow into the bathroom, in the bath tub, stacked around the bed, piled six feet high in pyramids around the easy chair and the reading lamp, books about travel, books about sailing, about the imagination, or even about—these are my favorite of all—nothing at all, just words upon the page, flowing with a rhythm like the flow of human blood, knives in the alley, bullets in the night, books exploding from the pantry, from the closets, from the stove, the oven, books, books, books, and lots of clothes, suits and shirts and socks and underwear and ties and sweaters and jackets (sports jackets and team jackets) and bowties and slacks and dungarees and tee shirts and the dirty but great car parked outside the apartment ready to make a get-away, get in the back, and I'll drive, we'll head north out of the city into the country, over the George W. Bridge and up the Palisades, and before an hour is gone, we'll be gone.

THE COUCH-POTATO HAMLET

Hamlet is not a young rebellious boy; he is a man who is unable to grow up. To act, to do, to perform—the gravediggers say. While acting is doing, performing often is neither acting nor doing. Witness Hamlet: he performs, he acts *out,* but not just acting. To act is not acting, though. Acting is performing, and this often is not doing. To Hamlet to think is to do and to act. I think, therefore I am acting, he seems to suggest by his inaction and yet his acting. Nearly as much of Hamlet is revealed in the gravediggers scene as in any other scenes in the play. The skull behind the flesh is revealed. Fear of death is often fear of living. Once he acts—when he does—when he is not merely performing, but simply is—Hamlet can think and do and act, even perform, as much as he wants, because he no longer fears death and thus no longer fears living. At thirty he understands his mother and he understands his father. He no longer feels the trauma of separation from them. He is his own man, and this singular man acts and does and performs as he pleases, according to his will and conscience.

BORGES AND I

The other one, the one called Borges, lives below me. I walk along Bow Street, and stop for a second, perhaps machine-like now, to look at the mural of George Washington in Union Square or contemplate the original American flag, part Union Jack, waving from the castle on Prospect Hill. I know of Borges because he is my landlord and he owns the restaurant below my apartment. Early in the morning the smell of Portuguese bread and garlic soup waft up to my open windows. I like poetry books, sports (running, basketball, boxing, and football), Irish literature, maps of any kind, binoculars, leather coats, and old photographs from my mother's family. Borges shares almost none of my interests, for he's a cook, but likes to act like a local wiseguy who often castigates tenants who put garbage in the wrong place—particularly if it messes up his grape-arbored, open-air restaurant's tables next to his building or, if like me, one complains for lack of heat, he begins to sound like Al Pacino in *The Godfather,* admonishing me "to do the right thing" or that "it is a question of honor." (I explain to him that it is not a question of honor but of heat; my apartment is freezing from the inside out.) It would be an exaggeration to say that ours is a hostile relationship; I let myself go on being, so that Borges may be paid his rent, yell at his wife and family, throw his tantrums in the basement galley of our building—I say galley instead of kitchen because all the Borges family are from the Azores, and I have noticed from living in Provincetown years ago that the Azoreans seem to prefer an architecture that resembles shipbuilding—but also to cook his overly large breakfast specials of ham, pancakes, blueberry waffles, eggs, potatoes, lettuce and tomato, coffee, bread, muffins, pastry, and melon or cream of wheat, so that

I and others in this town may go on writing our literature, painting, and having our thoughts. It is no great shakes to me to admit that he has gotten his restaurant reviews, guaranteeing his own immortality, while I plod ever onward into obscurity, writing my little paragraphs. Is it possible not to like him but to admire his cooking? Yes. I will disappear one day, but the memory of his blueberry pancakes will linger in this town for years to come. Little by little, my paychecks go to him to pay the rent, though I am cognizant of the fact of how he falsifies and exaggerates the manners of his tenants. Yet I shall stay here in Borges' building on Bow Street, seeing less of my old self each day. Weeks ago I tried to escape to the outskirts of the city, dreaming of points beyond, playing my teeny game with time and place, but now Borges owns all that. Thus it is not so much the piper who must be paid as Borges himself; each month rolls around faster than the last one, and he is at the door, knocking and demanding his rent.

Try to guess which one of us wrote this page.

THE DUCKS

Ducks never marry, and yet they mate forever, staying together until the end, and like us, this is no easy proposition, they leave the gaggle to become a brace, skyward, they fly from New York to New Hampshire, from the north country they migrate westward, to places like Rochester, New York, they swoop, they quack, they float, they fly, always wary of hunters as perhaps some of us are wary of them, or they shy from duck calls as phony as the blinds where the hunters and their retrievers wait, down and fat and aerodynamics, it is only in flight that we notice their grace, whereas the rest of the time it is only their fat-ass pond maneuvers which attract us, coming into their havens with bags of stale bread, we throw crumbs across the water, thinking to pacify them, but they are never kept by us, they take our offerings only to fly away in the morning, northward, eastward, this brace glides through clouds, scud water, and dive for minnows, and finally it is their patterns which intrigue us, kind of like an after-thought, a footprint they leave behind in the sky.

RED MAPLE

If I told you of the bush in the yard, its pale blossom, I mean, I was concerned, I think you would understand; and we spoke of other issues, the weather, the family, I think I never conveyed tension in my loins, a feeling so outside of family, I wanted to touch, touch your eyelids, your lips, your neck, your shoulders, impossible places for me or for you, I dreamed of legs and, I dreamed, because we had touched each other everywhere, I thought, I imagined we would touch, where you ache, I touched, I touched your legs, inside, I touch outside, I touch your breasts, I touch, I touch, I kiss, I kiss, oh little sparrow, you whisper, oh jackdaw and magpie. When I grab your belly, it is meat, it is real, it is healing, and you are heat, I have a heart, you are a woman, and I am this man, this is how the world began.

RED HERRING

This fish stinks! It's full of suds, the old creeps surface. Landlords! Landlords! It was a nice old building in an undeveloped neighborhood, the neighbors were good, we talked of sports and played sports in the park. After dark, this place became dangerous. Muggers abound! They want to sell me this apartment for millions of dollars. My God, this is the funkiest region in this city, I'm talking the yatter of tenement fire escape locutions all night long, the night quelled by discharges of mental patients on street corners, this is evil, man, this is funk, these landlords! landlords! landlords! these devils....

CHICLETS

Once I met a man, a German, who claimed to be from Ohio. I laughed, because he was funny; it was a sunny day, my floppy hat blowing in the wind, and my cat on a string for a walk. Ohio, I said, waving goodbye, thinking him Japanese. Chic Ohio—this is an example of conjuring an image out of nowhere, a kind of literary prestidigitation—Fockink gin in shrimp glasses, and when they finish, those claiming to be of Finnish ancestry, they speak of Vietnam; they take vitamins. The woman with the bob in her hair, her name is Alcestes; curiously enough, her husband, Bob, is on her arm, and their hosts have a dog named Bob. All of this I am making up, but that is my profession; you can't hold this against me, claim I am an unreliable witness because I never claimed to be otherwise. I have never been to Ohio, excepting that airplane ride from South Bend to New York, when the fuselage caught fire. Luckily, I sat next to Theodore Hesburgh, the president of Notre Dame, and slightly drunk (me, not him), I asked if he could intercede, "Oh, I've spoken with him already," he said, raising his eyes upward, and soon after that we landed in Ohio, Cleveland to be exact, and changed to another plane. But, really, I am thinking of this girl from French Lick, Indiana, who was a friend of my host back in South Bend. She claimed to attend Chico State in another state, and her state of mind was inebriated, to say the least. She did not drink Fockink gin, but she probably would have had it been offered, since she drank everything else in sight. What she did claim, too, was to know Larry Bird, though she also claimed never to have heard of Fockink gin, I grinned, drunk myself. Her beer drunk, she drank another beer from the can, sitting on her fanny at the bar in French Lick (her version of the story, at least), and told me that I should write about chic Ohio, oh my, she laughed, and then almost passed out. Instead, I offered her a Chiclet to get rid of that terrible smell she had on her breath from throwing up.

STEAK

Halibut steak, and Hollywood steak, as a child we ate filet mignon, frozen in boxes, hot from the docks where my father negotiated their transferal to our home. Oh, he was a card. Every night eleven people gathered—and quarreled—over steak and potatoes, all of the food lifted from piers on the West Side of Manhattan where Irish gangsters offered these tokens to my father as a kind of homage for letting them pilfer and rob the piers blind for thirty-five years, though he would not exactly put it that way. You have a roof over your head and a meal on the table, my father said, dreaming of the Depression. "A Piece of Steak" by Jack London is not London broil, it's fiction—about boxing, and you did not survive in my house unless you knew how to fight. These days I prefer tuna wrapped in seaweed with chopped scallions. My family, living and dying on potatoes and steak, would think me a snob to bring it up, but there is something at stake here. I eat, I pay rent. I walk, I strut, I sing, and these days I ain't drinking beer, I's sipping wine, I'm fine, I dine at the table with a fork and knife and a wife and child, and I love my wife but oh you kid. I eat fish, I eat salad. When a woman tells me I look like an Irish cop, I want to spit in her face, but instead I offer her another piece of cake. This is my fate, late at night, sitting on the couch, imagining myself a civilian once again.

SHINE

My blue shoes of soft leather do not take a shine, but the sun is out and I go for a walk, the rain of this past month gone, puddles in the street, slides in the earth, derailments in Vermont on the *Montrealer,* my favorite train from New York when I lived in New Haven. Not long ago, there used to be an upright piano in the bar car, and a reggae band rolled spliffs, we were stuck underneath the East River because the train to New England leaves the city via that tunnel into Long Island, then crosses back over Hell Gate and into the Bronx. There are not many cars in the city today, instead people are out walking. I'll wear my blue shirt and my gray pants, my blue shoes and my clean underwear. I'll walk two miles south, then see a play.

CEREBRAL CORTEZ

Ink, I oink, dreaming of Incas. (Jimmy Durante also comes to mind.) But an Aztec, educated in Ecuador, he visits and stays, and I open my heart to him, let him wear my hats, give him my rugs to wear like a sweater, and he opens my door to another family, these Mayans, oh so like Incas, their children must be put to death because they climb on the furniture, they play ball in the living room, climbing the bookshelves as if they were mountains. Out, out, you Aztecs! Back to your village to be slaughtered by my men. In my room of amber gold I listen to Jimmy Durante on the radio: Ink, Inka-dink-a-doo, A-inka, dinka-doo, means I love you. This is a rough translation of Cortez's sonnets, written in blood upon the rolling verdures of the Americas. Incas, write your congresswomen!

Under the Sign of Pisces

The fish like water, need water, live for it without which in cornfields or in the swelter of a jeep four-wheeling the dunes—but my thoughts never complete themselves these days in February, the old anxiety of aging in this season of crossed fish like stars or swords, I suppose. In another week I become another year older, hack of cigarettes, dull head of too much alcohol, night of carouse, etc. And in the dark hours of mid-winter before the solstice and St. Paddy's, the wind, usually severe, breathes like a heated babe in arms, the sun shines, and everyone is fooled but this fool, so fishy, his scales shine in sunlight and his teeth are bright like a sun, and his gills pump through streets, gasping for air. Only the fish knows winter is still and it is here for a while, next week it might snow or worse. On an aging planet these truths are obvious as wings on birds or trees with bare branches....

A Prose Poem Supposedly Written
by C. M. O'Shaughnessy

There are no poems about rice and no war stories I know about golf, this game in a landscape of man-made hazards that I loop like a wolf, I am a man, so darkly formed, only my shadow falls on these greens, and I sing of rice in this land of potatoes and sod, this Island shaped like a fish, a suburb of the great metropolis, I am a song of a generation who went to war, when there was no peace in our elders' hearts, I am a person seeking love, finding only hatred I came to expect nothing back in the world until I saw a lady on a hill, her stillness gave me life, and even after I took lives, and took another life, I am alive, I live as best I can, I circle the links like a wolf.

CASABLANCA

Long ago in Africa's northern country, I smoked opium in what I thought was the edge of the desert, a woman got fucked by a mule, it was 1965 or 1995, once upon a time when I worked on ships, I was young and up for it all, a seaman, a Merchant Mariner, never heard of Humphrey Bogart's movie or Peter Lorre, Sydney Greenstreet, I don't recall hearing the word Bacall either. My adventure was that desert smoke, sick for two days afterward, not just from the opium but from the rough seas, and sick of being on ship, I wanted to jump and go off into the Sahara, I wrote in my journal, I drank Heineken beer in the crew mess, watching the Puerto Ricans play dominoes, they argued like politicians or men on death row, I looked out the porthole, imagining monkeys all over Gibraltar, and in a day we docked in Palma de Majorca, I got laid in Chinatown, I ate chicken in the Kansas Bar, listened to flamenco in the crew pantry, always carried a big knife everywhere I went, and went off to Italy, stopped in Cannes, got caught in a police raid in a whorehouse in Madeira, but it all began in Casablanca, was there maybe five times, and still don't know a fucking thing about the place....

A Dream of a Porcelain Mouse

I found a rare blue-glazed white porcelain mouse in a tiny shop in Seoul, Korea and I brought it back to the United States with me. I took it to work, wanting to show it to a man who was considered an authority on these objects. As I walked down the hallway on the third floor of the building, his office next to mine, I removed the porcelain mouse, ready to show it to him. Going toward my office, this urge overcame me to give the man the porcelain mouse, since I really had no interest in it except as he had told me about them, and I thought it would be a nice gift. The nearer I got toward our offices the more playful I became with the delicate mouse, throwing it in the air, juggling it in my hands, right to left, left to right, hurling it skyward and barely catching it in my hands. The man stood at his door, key in hand, about to enter his own office, when I called out, "Hey, Georgie-boy, look at this porcelain mouse I found in Korea," and he stepped forward, a smile coming across his face, but it quickly turned to panic when he saw how I handled the delicate object, tossing it from hand to hand, flinging it in the air, pretending to miss my catch, it teetered on the tips of my fingers as he approached, I bobbled it, and when he came up to me, I let it drop, bursting in a million pieces on the marble floor. George looked as though he were about to cry, and I shrugged my shoulders, removing my own key, and jiggling open the door, which usually stuck, I smiled at him, now kneeling, trying to salvage some of the light blue-tinged white pieces of porcelain, its shape no longer resembling a mouse or anything animate or alive, but a fracture of molecules, some of them catching the fluorescent light and sparkling. "These mice can't be all things to all people," I said....

51

THIS ROOM

I speak of the voice, but I almost mean the eye and how the senses create pictures in the mind, it is a kind of talk that turns into a film or a painting, a crazy passion, I admit. The cover of this book is another thing, make it new, the old poet said, and I thought of a kind of architecture for the living to see or a song for the ears, let the eye learn to trust itself, and the voice sees little pictures. There is a kind of blue turning into green, angles of intent, the struts, what looks out from a high window is not the same as what is seen inside. This book is about the voice, a crazy passion, I admit, it was written in my sleep, breathing all over the pages, like someone else letting blood, I simply talked and it came into a picture of itself, a form. The cover is another thing entirely, something new and fresh, I hope, a kind of architecture of the mind, I guess, but also a passionate utterance of the eye, seeing and believing, the eye to see what the ear hears or what the hand touches, this is abstraction turned into a little picture. If I were to verbalize the picture, it would be a kind of blue which is almost green, angles too because I like them, and struts (the architecture), but a kind of moonwalk of the soul, I would ask that this picture think of me as it thinks, simply thinks, of whatever it wants to think about, and desires. But the circle is too political, and old-fashioned, a drum round which the natives dance, forever coming back to a beginning, but never moving forward, I look ahead, I look backward, I look back, and then move on. Spheres enter spirals, the old geometry, one and one equals, or from the sphere comes a spiral, hot and liquid, burning towards its center.

HELEN AGAIN

After an exhaustive day of breaking in a new Polonius and a new—the third one—Ophelia, O'Shaughnessy came from the evening's performance exhausted but unable to sleep, and so he sat at his desk, writing notes. He now had a Hamlet notebook in which he jotted observations. For instance, he wrote, "Hamlet is a prism into which light is poured and out of which a spectrum occurs. He is a mirror, reflecting his own time, but also reflecting the dramaturgy of theatre history back before time and also outward until the present moment. He is the Prince of Denmark. These facts taken together, bluntly, softly, subtly, or all-at-once, turn him into the labyrinth as well. You may never exit from *Hamlet* once you have entered; in that sense, the play is the Twilight Zone. You become Hamlet even after you played him and are now doing other parts. Suddenly you appear on stage in a contemporary farce, and instead of doing your lines, you quote from the play: 'The time is out of joint. O cursed spite. / That ever I was born to set it right.' Hamlet is not so much sponge as prism, becoming everyone who ever came in contact with him. Then, again, he is nothing at all, his words vanish, never to be remembered again, or if remembered, not as yours or his, but as William Shakespeare's, that eternal flesh and blood. Yet I knew that in order to understand Hamlet I needed to get beyond this obsession and go back further than the Renaissance; I had to journey beyond tragedy, back when there were choral odes. Seneca and the Romans would not do, although they did more than their share to make Hamlet who he is. After all, the young Shakespeare was weaned on the violent imagination of the Romans. I needed to go back further into the dramaturgy of being, beyond Gertrude, before the Sophoclean shuffle. It had something to do with the dithyramb where Hamlet was. Before Thespis and Arion. It went back to Helen once again."

IMAGINEERING

The imagineers convention was held on the first Saturday of the month in the great ballroom of the oldest hotel in the center of the city. Lots of laypeople came. Also, a busload of hookers arrived, though none of the imagineers would admit that the hookers had been called by one of them; they claimed that some outsiders had called the hookers to play a practical joke on the convention of imagineers. At the first conference a fist fight broke out about whether imagineering had more to do with physics and robotics than with the imagination and the life-of-the-mind crowd's hobby-horses. One faction of imagineers wanted to visit the rock dedicated to John Lennon in the middle of Strawberry Fields in Central Park across from the Dakota Hotel; this group was later expelled from the convention for setting fire to the drapes in one of their hotel suites. Imagineers from around the world converged on the Staten Island ferry, proclaiming that it was liberated from Staten Island. Other imagineers declared that Staten Island was the newest state of mind. One faction from the West Coast claimed that imagineering was a male plot to undermine the gay, feminist, and Asian American movements. Several Nobel Laureates had cream pies thrown in their faces; this was a terrible mistake, everyone agreed. On the second-to-last day of the convention a dancing bear raced into the lobby of the hotel on a unicycle, juggling the twenty-one volumes of Charles Dickens' work. Of course, this was not really a bear, but rather a deranged publicist in a bear outfit hired by the steering committee to put some life into the moribund convention, and had more imagineers been awake at the hour in which the bear occupied the lobby of the old hotel, no doubt it would have caused a lot of excitement. As it turned out, only six people witnessed the spectacle, and only half that number could agree that it was a man in a bear costume on a unicycle juggling many volumes of books. Some thought it was a sloth on a tricycle. Others said that it was a panda—not really a bear—on Rollerblades, juggling timetables and periodic tables and tables of contents. You can never find two imagineers who will agree to anything in common these days. The convention ended on a sour note when an imagineer from Seattle pulled out an assault rifle and began to strafe the lobby with his automatic weapon. He was later subdued by the police; in fact, one of the officers shot him dead.

Castor and Pollux

Pollux earned his keep breaking heads, opening cuts in men's eyebrows, pounding kidneys until they pissed blood. It's a dirty business, boxing, the old-timers in the legendary gyms will say. Blood in the eye, searching for a brother, the horseman, Polydeuces. It takes no Marquis of Queensberry to know that the journey from Youngstown, Ohio to Hell is one punch. Red Everlast gloves dance with St. Elmo's fire, hungry, heated, lethal, Ladies and Gentlemen, I give you the lightweight champion of the world, Ray "Boom-Boom" Mancini, who descends from the ring to his home, waiting to hear if Deuk-Koo will come out of coma, but the challenger is brain-dead. You hear that foreign name in the wind around the closed factories of this industrial town, the pigeons cooing it all day and night—coo, coo, deuk-coo. Yet everyone knows that it is not easy being of the Dioscuri, the brothers Gemini, half the year with Zeus in Heaven, the rest spent in Hell, where it is hotter than a blast furnace or smelter. Still, the champion must go on being the champion. Those are the rules and regulations, in and outside the ring. Ray fought, and won, the championship to revenge the slight of a fickle world that let a world war intervene in his own father's quest for a title. And back in Korea, Kim's mother donated his strong body parts to hospitals for implants, and then she faded into the countryside of her peninsula, where she did the only decent thing she could think of, having committed the unpardonable Confucian sin of outliving her son. Mrs. Kim killed herself.

PART THREE

HOMER'S MOTHER

Other children have pimples and acne, dreaming of their proms. But he will have none of that, singing in the shower like Stevie Wonder, blind and oblivious, fabricating warriors in his head, the beauty that was Helen, the warrior Ulysses, the man that would become known as Achilles. Other children write poems that rhyme like Hallmark greeting cards. His songs defy categorization, sometimes flute-like, often inspired by the sound of the lyre, his associates often speak of his vast blues collection, spinning afternoons away listening to John Lee Hooker, Leadbelly and Robert Johnson, the king of the Delta blues singers. Oh, and of course Ray Charles. He owns nearly every record that the blind pianist recorded, and now has digitalized his collection, converting everything to compact discs. When asked about the Pepsi-drinking singer, Homer reminds people that Charles' real name was Robinson. Then the blind sage speaks further about the blind singer. "Walker Smith chose the name Ray Robinson," Homer says, "in order to fight when he was too young to be fighting. He became known as Sugar Ray." But among those who do not understand such matters, it might be asked what this has to with Ray Charles, the blues and country-western and pop singer? But if you have to ask, Jelly used to say, you'll never understand. "Ray Charles' real name was Robinson," Homer repeats. "The Raylettes did backup for him. He became one of the greatest singers and pianists America has ever known. If his voice was like sugar, it was with a touch of bourbon. But listen here: Ray Charles Leonard was named after the singer, not the fighter, because it was the singer whom his parents loved, and yet after he fought, Ray Leonard became known as Sugar, because he reminded everyone of Ray Robinson. Do I make myself clearer, nuncle?" No one is sure who made the connection, or at least who first made it, though probably it was Homer's mother who reminded everyone that all these men had one thing in common, and that was that all of them were named Ray. That two of them were Sugars, though the third was sugar-free. Uh-huh, they said. One was blind; another was almost blinded. (Leonard's detached retina.) Yet if you were to x-ray these great men, like Homer, they all had bones, like mortals did, and all needed rest and nurturing. All were made of muscle and tissue, and each had a life with a storyline, each was a gifted black man in a white world, though race was something that Homer did not personally understand, his belief being that all men were of the gods conceived and made in the likeness thereof. Yet each of these Rays was a mortal man, though each did something timeless and maybe immortal, or so Homer told everyone who chose to listen or ask. Ray Robinson proved this by getting old, then dying while he was still in his sixties. Alzheimer's, they say. But that Sugar Ray was the greatest fighter, pound for pound, Homer says, and that must be worth something as a ticket into Heaven and immortality. "If there is poetry in this," Homer spoke onward, "it is because a ray of light streams through the window, though I am blind to the light. Still, I am sensitive to heat, and my arm feels the light, and I am sensitive to sounds, and the sunlight cracks over the wood floors, and I hear the dust motes drifting downward through space into the cracks in the floor. Also, there is music in boxing, just as there is a fight in Ray Charles' music, or maybe I am only listening to this music in ways that it has never been listened to before, say back in the fifties when Mr.

Charles first became a noticeable commodity in the record world." But Homer stopped speaking when he realized that his friends were not interested in talking about anything unless it had to do with the Super Bowl or the upcoming NCAA tournament, and whether it was beach weather or just-going-to-the-movies weather, or whether or not it even mattered at all, their lives being worn and suburban, their loves being for bubble-gum princesses and princes in the latest soap-opera'd movies at the mall. Ah, Homer, blindman on the bluff, stoked up on verse and vice-versa'd, the adverse and the perverse, the sublime and the criminally insane on dates with stars. Most of the time he rode a bicycle in circles, scheming of ways to invent the Pacific Ocean. He tried to imagine the Grand Canyon and yawned. After all, his heroes were mythical creatures from the ancient regime, a time when to talk of Persians and Macedonians was all the rage. His time had no Pepsi-Cola machines to run to, no athletes full of dementia pugilisticana. Cassandra did not wear culottes, seer of another sire, sighted but silent, that ghost of the future past, perfect in her silence, imperfect in her fate, just as your own fate would be imperfectly rendered, yet lasting through the millennia, a plethora of sounds comparable to the best that Elvis Presley had to offer, or the poems of the late Jim Morrison, the poems of Eugene McCarthy.

Three Dreams

1.

One of them a friend I had not spoken with in some time, he stood off in the corner of the bar, not talking or saying anything, not even hello. I was troubled by this, but I did not confront him at all, and instead kept drinking with the people I was with, saying to myself, it don't mean a thing, fuck it, that son of a bitch. But when I awoke, I was full of sweat, because I hadn't had a drink in days, and I realized that the friend in the corner was myself, back to drinking because the man I was would always be drunk.

2.

The same bar: I drink with a public-relations guy who likes Jack Kerouac, and insists that I know him, I mean Jack Kerouac, only I insist that I don't know him, either the public relations man or Jack Kerouac. I'm too young to know either of these people, I think. Then she walks in with a black woman, and you have the feeling that they both just made love, and had a good time of it, so now they want their drinks, and she nods at me as cool as a debutante, which she ain't, believe me, and I mouth hello silently, not saying anything, only afterward she comes over to me and asks if we can slip away to her apartment because, seeing my face, she says, she has become real horny. This only happens in my dreams as the woman, in real-time and daylight into night, detests me with a passion.

3.

Another crime against domestic order has been committed, and I am the leading suspect, which is not to be mistaken for the leading man in a play. I get my visitation rights weekly. I pay the alimony monthly. I stay away from the ex whenever it is needed. This is real, only it's in a dream, so I guess it is not real, but feels like it is. Did I dream I was playing Hamlet? It seems so long ago, so far away, so other than now, so unlike me to take on a part such as Hamlet, and then not deliver, to get lost in a million other things, though mainly I am caught up in a web of thoughts, thinking, thinking, never acting, never taking an action, I am there, but not here, I am over there, in the corner, thinking, thinking. A friend offers me a photograph of a naked woman, his girlfriend, and asks me what do I think of her breasts? I say that they look great. The next thing I know I am on a beach with her, and she is naked (my friend's girlfriend, I mean, but not my friend who is nowhere to be found), asking me what I think of her breasts. Spectacular, I say, and she asks me to touch them. What do you think now? she asks. Even better, I say. Kiss them, she orders. I do. Lick them, she demands, though her voice also has an edge of pleading in it, and I do, and then she drops her hand between my legs, and I don't wake until everything is finished on the beach, though I never return to the bar where my friend started this all by showing me the naked photograph of his girlfriend.

The Comics

The scrawny cat's maledicta balloon inflates with jarns, quimps, grawlix and nittles. (A lot of comic strip *kaplooie* to you uninitiated.) Meanwhile, the mouse hightails it, feet a blur of blurgits, its gloved digiton thrashing as plewds cascade off its wiry little head. What would this world be like without a dog named Spike with his thorny collar, behind him a cloud of briffit, and staggeration across the lucaflects and cross-hatching of its vicious paws. (Find yourself a good cartoonist to explicate this text, ya lousy bum ya.) Spike will get the cat Arnold who hates the mouse Frank. Waftarom emit from an open manhole cover, solrads ripple the street, while spurls drift out of a drunk's head, his burps marked by squean, his eyes nothing more than oculama. (Yeah, well maybe if you read the funnies instead of those goddamn fancy-schmancy books, you'd understand what I'm talking about here, ya jerk from Hoboken.) So the dog knocks the drunk into the manhole, the cat scrams up a hawthorn tree, and Frank the mouse goes off for a beer and cigarette with his friend, good old Spike the dog.

THE GREEKS

The Greeks begin and end for me with Helen, O'Shaughnessy thought, still sipping that strong Puerto Rican coffee at La Rosita de Broadway. Like some of their statues, now fragmentary, armless, nose chipped, Helen is only a fragment today. We do not know her totality. Part of this fragmentation has to do with the patriarchal world of ancient Greece. There is Zeus above; Achilles, Agamemnon, and Odysseus below, and at the start of Homer's *Iliad*. This sphere of patriarchy is quite pervasive, filling every slot in the Homeric epic. Witness Agamemnon's response, when asked to give up his concubine in order to make a truce:

> Here you stand again
> before the army, giving it out as oracle
> the Archer made them suffer because of me,
> because I would not take the gifts
> and let the girl Khryseis go; I'd have had her
> mine, at home. Yes, if you like, I rate her
> higher than Klytaimnestra, my own wife.
> She loses nothing by comparison
> in beauty or womanhood, in mind or skill.
> (*Robert Fitzgerald translation*)

This is not macho so much as it is supermacho, the macho man himself talking, almost like a swaggering wrestler or a welterweight pug. This manliness only becomes peculiar in extremis, where it seems to invert itself, becoming nearly effeminate. (See Pinter's *Homecoming.*) Helen to these men is not only a woman, not merely that; she is a cunt, both a blessing and a curse, a beautiful object that all want to possess and hold, be inside of. Helen is possession.

Again, O'Shaughnessy thought, I have no ultimate answer, drawn from observation of the ancient world, to make a point of how these men of Homer's world felt. Helen, in Homer, as well as in Aeschylus' *Oresteia,* is only shadow and shade, a mere fog, a kind of erotic possibility that pulses in the background. Talk about subtext; that is all she is. One long panting subtext. It is not until Book Three of *The Iliad* that Helen is made concrete, and when she is, this is all Homer offers:

> She (Iris) found her weaving in the women's hall
> a double violet stuff, whereon inwoven
> were many passages of arms by Trojan
> horsemen and Akhaians mailed in bronze—
> trials braved for her sake at the war god's hands.
> Approaching her, swift Iris said.
>
> > "Come, dearest,
> come outside and see the marvelous change
> in Trojans and Akhaians!

But where is Helen? Is this a woman? Where is her flesh? Those answers do not come until the next stanza. First we are given a metaphysical Helen, that body which drove men to war has not surfaced yet. We are told of her heart filled with "smoky sweetness and desire." Still, no Helen. We are told of her clothes: she "cloaked herself in silvery veils." Of her emotional state it is said that she let "a teardrop fall and left her chamber." And yet when she appears before these warriors, one of them says:

> We cannot rage at her, it is no wonder
> that Trojans and Akhaians under arms
> should for so long have borne the pains of war
> for one like this.

Another old man adds that she is "unearthliness," "a goddess the woman is to look at." Yet another adds a sour note: "Ah, but still, still, even so, being all that she is, let her go in the ships and take her scourge from us and from our children." Priam bids the dear child to sit, and he does not blame her for anything: "You are not to blame," he says,

> I hold the gods to blame for bringing on
> this war against the Akhaians, to our sorrow.

Even without her physically transformed before us, O'Shaughnessy thought, eating his flan and drinking his *café con leche,* Helen does speak. She says that "revere you as I do,"

> I dread you, too, dear father.   Painful death,
> would have been sweeter for me, on that day

I joined your son, and left my bridal chamber,
my brothers, my grown child, my childhood friends!
But no death came, though I have pined and wept.
Your question, now: yes, I can answer it:
that man is Agamemnon, son of Atreus,
lord of the plains of Argos, ever both
good king and a formidable soldier—
brother to the husband of a wanton ...
       or was that life a dream?

The inner character of Helen—contrite, sorrowful, wanton—is bestowed upon us. Still, she is transparent, and it is only given to us, further along, that she is "tall in her gown, in her silver cloak," and again we return to her identifying men in the crowd. Menelaus and Alexandros are to do battle for Helen, and nothing more is said of her until Aphrodite snatches Alexandros away from the battlefield and then entreats Helen to his bedchamber. Helen is only whorish in the minds of men, for amid the sisterly ways of women, she seems gentle and unforbidding; she pleads with Aphrodite not to let her go to that chamber.

I shall not join him there! It would be base
if I should make his bed luxurious now.
There will be such whispering
among the Trojan women later—

Helen deals with the womanly goddess Aphrodite, and she is no match for the greater woman-goddess, and so she goes to the bedchamber of Paris. Her greetings to her lover are full of barbs and taunting.

> Home from the war? You should have perished there,
> brought down by that strong soldier, once my husband.
> You used to say you were the better man,
> more skilled with our hands, your spear. So why not
> challenge him to fight again?

Suave Paris asks Helen to drop her bitter words.

> Let us drop war now, you and I,
> and give ourselves to pleasure in our bed.
> My soul was never so possessed by longing,
> not even when I took you first aboard
> off Lakedaimon, that sweet land, and sailed
> in the long ships.

Yes, Helen arouses men, O'Shaughnessy thought, there is no doubt about that. But what is it about her that arouses them? We are told, in the heat of battle, that Paris is eroticized by her, is all heat. That they go to his bed of inlaid ivory and there "these two made love." This only interests me, O'Shaughnessy thought, because each Ophelia is an actress that so far has excited no interest in me in an erotic sense, and perhaps that is so Hamlet-like, and yet I believe that my ultimate Hamlet will be a man aroused by Ophelia, because he sees Helen in her eyes, and wants, like Paris, to possess her in the heat of battle. Otherwise, all is loss, and folly. It is his hope that this third Ophelia that Andrei has imported from abroad will do the trick, that she will excite poor O'Shaughnessy into playing the ultimate Hamlet because he will see Helen in his Ophelia's eyes.

"Oh, that this too too solid flesh would melt," he said.

"*Mas café?*" the waitress asked.

"*Si, si,*" he answered. "*Mas café, por favor.*"

M. G. Stephens

Spring

A green odor—it must be April!

MOTHER

What's it matter? She was only your mother. There are plenty more where she came from. They all know how to dance backwards in high heels like Ginger Rogers, reciting Shakespeare's sonnets. Some even recite backwards and in high heels, spinning plates balanced on long wooden sticks on the tip of their nose. She's only your mother, and this isn't even her day.

The Guinness Book of the Dead

From moor to hencoop, out up to the ruins, clurachaun-man with his fish-eyed woman lurches into cliff-face, face to face with the dawning world. From these loops in the terrain, they loped, not yet despairing, they were full of their hopes as they badgered each other about fire and food, and when it seemed futile, they fucked in the peat, they procreated, creating havoc, and sons and daughters and flippery creatures not yet son and daughter; they sweated in the rain, planting rows of roots, they slaughtered kine, and then feasted with fermented cups or drank the grain from burnt eggshells, toasting their stupid lives. Once the land formed a pattern, they forced their children out into those fields, squandering their songs through the pain in their arms, they plodded through the interminable swamps, making art of old skulls, making conversation of lost paths, drinking each other silly into the cold wet damp night, lodging among themselves, their tribe, the children of children from children, and others came, finding warmth at the fire, and so the dead went from life into hellfire or heaven, and came back sainted, pluralized, whispering other songs, until King Quark dirged on his farts, clearing out the encampment of children, forcing the barriers between the heathen pagan satyrs and the dark-voiced others, talkers of three-headed gods like shamrocks, bleaters of ramifications to the sexless Saxon and angled tongues of Angles, not to mention the normative wonders of the northerners, and the abnormal ways of the Normans. Fuck them all in the throat, King Quark barked, and screw their pigs' asses into eternity, okay, okay, the men yattered, and the women loomed, making sweatery things, making wordless murmured tunes on their tongues in the dungheaps of Quark's castles, the dreary drumlins, the pulsing vegetal gardens, the squared-off circles where those demented by fermentations went to fight their hearts away, bashing faces and stomachs, and lowing until the break of dawn.

Bukowski Blues

I stop into the local saloon and see Freddy the bartender wearing this weird tee shirt, Yo, Freddy, I say, is that them crazy girls I met in here a couple of months ago, meaning the logo on the tee shirt, is it those crazy girls' artistic enterprise or whatever they called it? Corny Mike, he whispers, one of them is sitting two bar stools away, and then I say to the bartender, but you have to be crazy to talk to me and they were talking to me, so they must be crazy. I remember that in this conversation their dreams were impossible, and of course I like people with dreams like that, and they were tough and feminine, they were not full of shit, they wouldn't take any shit, and they acted as if they didn't give a shit, but that was the point—they did. They gave a shit. The one who wore a yellow hat said, Where do you get off calling me a girl? I thought Cyndi Lauper made the word "girl" popular, I said, drunk now, and, besides, I said, I'm twice your age, you're a girl all right. You're 36 years old, asshole, she said, and that's hardly twice my age. How do you know how old I am? I asked. Call me a chick, she says, *oye, chica,* she says, calling her friend, *oye, chica,* I said, *que pasa, que linda, es muy agradable, si, como no!* This doofus motherfucker called me a girl. A girl! the other laughed, I'll cut his balls off if he keeps talking like that.

THE ROOM

I have known this room for many years, inside and day in and day out, books on the walls, in their shelves, typewriter, chairs, table, ordinary things that are not the same since you walked in, sat down, and we talked. When was the first time? It was the autumn, I guess, leaves turning, tumbling, the wind cutting the cool air. You looked like someone I had known, but that quickly changed to—you looked like no one I'd ever seen, some dream I had of a woman maybe, pale and dark-haired, voluptuous, shy, I thought that kissing your hands was better than fucking most women, I did, or seeing you, bundled in thick sweater, your lips, your eyes, that little scar on your face, I was gone, my central nervous system went awol, wacked-out, I adored you. This room has not changed in many years, and even before I inhabited it, it was still the same, wood floors, walls of no particular color, pictures, pens and pencils, endless paper, and the room still does not change. I walked in and walked out, different, not differently, I had my strut, my attitude, cocky, brash, stubborn, I was not the same anymore. Thought of your shoulders, the flesh around your belly, of neck and tensions, rising, falling, that passionate moment, forever altering this room, its inhabitants.

THE MODEL

Her talk was of body parts, the hands, the legs, from the shoulder up to the head, she said she was disproportionate elsewhere, where, I wondered, looking for these parts, my breasts, she said, they are too large, oh no, I thought, just right....

CHRISTMAS EVE

Two days before St. Stephen's Day, I wore my coat of leather and down, it was so cold, the bells were clay and the earth was rock-like ground. Into the salt of early winter, the light of day was low, iron and blue vein, breath of feathers, breath of frozen words, tongue-frozen, I walked in my gritted bones, boots of synthetics, Thinsulate's wonder, Gore-Tex, Duofold underwear, sheepskin and flask of Irish, breathe the razor-blade wind, streets empty of people, streets of gray stone, purple wreaths, heather really, I go....

Spring Comes In

The devil has my soul, the heartache rams, I am, I am, I think
I am, therefore, therefore, foreplay is in the air, the shuttlecock
wings, a musical shuttle grows like a tumor in my arm, I am,
I am, I definitely am, the cows do moo, the birds are singing,
my ex-wife sings, too, my daughter hums along, I am singing,
I am, I am, I sing, goddamn I am, god-fucking-damnit I am,
I am, I am....

HOUSE OF REPTILES

It had been many years since our families got together, or my older brother and I had talked and seen each other. My wife and child, his ex-wife, their children, we had the picnic at the zoo, and afterward went to the House of Reptiles, my brother and I watched intently as the reticulated python strangled a rooster to death, there you go, he said, though not meaning it as a kind of metaphor of our relationship, we were more like wild terriers, anyhow, fiery, and never willing to end a fight, with ourselves or others, *semper fi* could have been our motto, because, like marines, we were willing to sacrifice our bodies to the dumbest causes, football, for instance, or bar brawls (the family honor), but that wasn't how it happened, there was no semper fi because our oldest brother got fucked up in the Army, the other one had asthma, and I was under arrest when drafted (a drug charge), so that all we did, years later, was catch up on family stuff and then met up with our families at the crocodile pit, the disappointed looks on their faces, later, in another pavilion, the tropical rain forest, which read: Thunderstorm Temporarily Discontinued. Later, we watched rattlesnakes and then said our goodbyes.

HER FACE

And I remember that first time I saw you, standing out there on line like a flower in December or snow in summer, you were there like that. You came into the room like a lily or a dragon, the heat in me was fiery, and I bathed that night, just to cool off. In your splendors I have thought of you, young, alive, wonderful, and it makes me jump or dance. Let me show you how I dance around the coffee table or jig about the apartment, on my toes, in the clouds, up in the sky, helium-headed, ether-silly, Old Lead Foot, he comes home to foxtrot about. But it was not only that movement through my rooms, I dreamed about your face for seven days running, coming out of sleep I nearly saw you in the room. What did I say? I asked you for the time—was it time to get up?—or asked you for a drink that afternoon, or maybe I asked you for a glass of water right there, I can't remember now, maybe it was to ask you out for dinner that night at nine. This I remember, though; your face lit up the room.

WINTER SKY

Summer's interminable vagaries, even in the mountains, even at the shore, leaked into autumn, so that I was lifeless in October with the heat, the green, the sweats. Let summer end on Labor Day, the cool breezes of September break over the nightfall, and when you come to me or I to you, it will be in down or sweaters, with boots from the closet, hats and bloomers, brandy for the end of day. Here it is November, and a week of heats, but by Friday, coming back from the endless rehearsals, the sky is low and gray, the winds whip, the air goes cold, there is no sun by five o'clock. That's what I like most before the frost, how the weather comes out like that, and then goes down, fading to black. Full of clothing and knocking pipes, steam heat, warm red wine, the words swell.

Post-Courtly Love

I will dance out to you in my blue Nikes, my arms cutting the air as though with swords. If you come down my street in a coach and horses, their thick whinny above the grid-locked traffic noises, if you come through the vale, through meadows, through fog of night, through the wet grasses, your hem dragged over wet grass and mute stones, I'll come out to meet you in my sweat pants and trench coat, cigarette dangling from mouth, intrigues on my tongue, and this hand to adorn you, high-boned woman, lady of my life. If you arrive in the morning, hands full of rolls and paper cups of coffee, I'll provide the newspaper, the table, the conversation. I'll wait by the monkey bars, my hands full of roses, as you trip the speed bumps, as you bring songs and autobiography.

Goat Song

Dionysos' feminine balls hung like a China bull's. He danced his kordax like a horny goat. In green pastures. Yellow curls hung from his head and lapped his oriental cheek. And his animal eyes bled through with spring wine. Women galloped. Old women clawed the ground. Men ran wild like ponies. Young boys grew cleft. Ungulates trotted with swollen rectums. Blue balls. Raw vaginas. Milk ran from breasts. Old men in leopard skins rubbed their androgynous teats. Mythos moans and aelos songs. Two-pronged goat songs. Hounds lapped lukewarm milk. Maids lapped semen and blood. Fever. Libations. Frenzy. Old bulls in pasture. Calves were eaten, barely cooked. Virgins were threatened with eating, and then were licked by Dionysos. Dionysos was eaten, too, and grew inside the girls. Men barfed wine. Screwed. Passed out. Were blown by goats. Lapped by virgins. Eaten by old women in heat. Grapes. And more grapes. Grapes were crushed between white thighs. Grapes pressed between bosoms. Wine mixed with mother's milk. Wine. Semen. The bloods. Grapes were fermented and drunk. Who believes, it was said, in Dionysos, is Dionysos. But who disbelieves, let his limbs be torn off. Who does not know Dionysos, let his own mother eat him. Who will not worship Dionysos, let the penis be ripped out. Let those who love most be those who destroy love that is not Dionysos. Who worships Dionysos must eat Dionysos. Let us cook the God on a spit. Yet mother ate her son. Sister stripped father. Baby cries. Song. Goat song. Aelos song. Plucked lyres. Grape song. Song of panting virgin. Song of wet vulva. Song of wine. Virgins. Blood song. Wine. Pubic song. Menstrual dance. Goat's in the meadow. Goats. Song of Dionysos. Phrygian song. Love that is half beast. To human beat. Love of leopard-skinned old men. Dance of kordax bump. Bluster. Bone grind. Pelvic grind. Dance of swollen phallus. Spring song. Dionysos.

SEEMS, MOTHER, IS ...

My mother is a teardrop. Mother is a rose without a thorn. My mother had sixteen children, nine of them lived, sucking her paps. Mother is forever young, growing old with wrinkles. My mother was a nurse who believed in the fertile sex act. My mother is very small. Mother had so many children, I cannot believe what she endured. Mother knows how to laugh and to cry. Mother wrapped herself in a veil of sorrow to find her joy. My mother's face is the shape of the sun and of her sons and of her daughters. My mother formed the embryos on a blue stone in watercolor. Mother floats in a gauze of vicissitudes. My mother's expression can be terrifying or it can be of love. She sees madness, religious fanatics, alcoholics, artists, musicians, writers, husband and wife translunar fits. And mother calls this love. My mother made each bed each day and made each sandwich for lunch. Seventy-five thousand sandwiches in her life. On Mother's Day, I called her on the telephone and she told me about my brother in Connecticut, about his horse and about how he looked like Saint Joseph as he rode, his long hair caught in the wind. (My brother had been arrested in New York City on a drug charge and part of his parole meant moving to this place in rural Connecticut where he worked with wolves, and eventually he rented a farm where he had a horse and dogs and other animals.) My mother said the room in her hotel had six windows: her idea of luxury. My mother flew to Los Angeles to be with her two pregnant daughters (one married, one not). She wanted to be with the husbandless daughter to give comfort near parturition. My mother liked my first book, she said I was very funny and very sick. That I looked too severe on the book jacket. Mother said I looked like an Irish scholar. Serious, dark, cloistered, alone, devoutly sacrilegious. Mother is sacrosanct. My mother gives speeches at her Alcoholics Anonymous meetings. She had six brothers and sisters herself, raised in a big house in Brooklyn. My mother now loves Jesus and Krishna. My mother: a rose without a thorn. Small as a teardrop. Saint Elizabeth, Mary's mother; Rose, my mother. She makes novenas, smokes Salem cigarettes, joined Weight Watchers, had her gall bladder out, grew very pale from this. My mother: a teardrop, rose. Rose is my mother. Rose is a teardrop. Rose is a rose without a thorn. My mother is a muse. Mother visited my oldest brother in the mental hospital. And she once visited me in New Haven. But I was not home, and so she left a note, scrawled in her Catholic schoolgirl handwriting. My mother: a woman. What her sex suffers! Mother is not politically liberated because she is not political. Mother is not religiously liberated because she believes in God. Mother is not sexually liberated because she had sixteen children. She is not free. Yet my mother is liberated. She believes in the rose. My mother is the miracle of the rose, so small and so sweet, tough and liberated, and so delicious. O, Rose. Proud Rose. My mother: a tear, a rose drop. Rose …

CLEAR LIGHTS AND RED LIGHTS

"From the time of the Greek and Roman mimes there has been a connection between theatre and prostitution," Andrei the director said at the weekly cast meeting. "This juxtaposition of the oldest and the second oldest professions begins in antiquity and has never stopped its symbiosis," he went on. "It is evident in the Dark Ages, the Middle Ages, the Renaissance—in Shakespeare's theatre, Moliere's, the commedia dell'arte—and comes full circle into our present time." As Andrei went on and on, I turned from our present Ophelia, this Abigail from Ohio named Ms. Morrison, a youngcomer on the regional boards, and stared instead at Andrei's wife, a woman nearly twenty years his junior, a peasant girl, it seemed, her face beautiful and innocent as his was ugly and experienced and so full of itself. Hers was empty of illusions about self. Her skin was spotless scrubbed, and though the blouse she wore probably was bought in a boutique on St. Mark's Place, it made her look even more peasant, and, oddly, more Ophelian. Our eyes caught and locked, and then a blush ran over her cheeks. Her husband droned on and on: "Any visitor to Broadway knows that the legitimate houses are sandwiched between the goings and comings of Times Square streetwalkers, massage parlors, porn houses, strip joints, whorehouses fronting as dance parlors, palm reading storefronts which sell sex, etc." When I looked up again, wondering to myself why I listened to this boring screed by this egotistical director who usurped our time well beyond rehearsals—after all, we had been running now for several weeks and he still called these ridiculous meetings where he harangued about nothing, and we had to dutifully listen, week after week—I noticed that Nadja, Andrei's wife, stared singlemindedly at me. Her husband continued: "Even in so austere a setting as the Yale Repertory Theatre in New Haven, directly across the street and running down Chapel to Park Streets, the hookers and their pimps gather and do business, not unlike they have done for centuries, in the shadow of the legitimate stage." I recalled the rumors circulating in the company now; Andrei fired his Ophelias week after week because he had affairs with all of them, and when he tired of one, he hired another Ophelia. Yet the Ophelia of Ophelias was in his midst, his very own wife Nadja, this peasant beauty. "Of course," he went on at his most bombastic, "there seems to be no clear reason for this historical juxtaposition between legitimate theatre and the theatre of the street." I whispered aloud, "Performance," and he said *excuse me,* and I repeated the word, the connection between them, *performance,* but he chose to ignore it and went on: "It suffices to say that this relationship is long-lasting, and worth investigating. Herewith are some observations, from antiquity to the present, about this unique juxtaposition. Try to assimilate what I have said into your performances," and he got up and left the room, followed shortly after that by the new Ophelia, followed by the stage manager, other actors, crew, etc., until no one was left but Nadja and me, and when I invited her for coffee, she accepted, and almost immediately, we were upstairs in a Times Square hotel, screwing our brains out, the true Hamlet, the true Ophelia, while that damn Claudius of a director screwed his version of Ophelia in a hotel across town.

Jocasta's Bath

Through the long night I did not see Helen but instead dreamt of Jocasta as though she were Gertrude, but also she was Ophelia (Nadja) and even Hamlet (myself). Like Venus stepping naked from her bath she pinned a yellow chiton at the neck, a linen of soft hanging folds, suggesting upturned breasts and her supple waist, and her gown had no sleeves but fell to the ground with a train, she licked her lips and whispered, Oh, Hamlet, pin my tunic at the shoulder, and Oh Hamlet, help me to put on this himation, pin it and draw it around me and under the right arm, throw it over the left shoulder, oh and rid yourself of those tragic boots, darling, and I can't worry about a plague on our cattle when my thighs burn worse than Phaedra's, touch me and oh I need it worse than Helen did, lick my neck, pretend that I am Ophelia, as Aphrodite and Dionysos will be oh so honored, we'll be like the slaves and do it in the stables on top of the warm goat flops, and oh there's nothing underneath my chiton, nothing, Hamlet, but this regal warmth, oh and I need you tonight. When I woke, I said to myself, a few more weeks for this limited run, and then you'll find yourself a contemporary play to act in, and, if that fails, you'll go back to bartending.

THE FUGITIVE ART

From the Greeks I always imagined two actors, brothers
perhaps, in this chancy profession, they love to sing, recite
poems, to imitate, though their elders call it "dissembling,"
this fugitive art they practice at wine festivals, drunken revels,
where they come home pummeled and sated, laughing over
jokes and lines swapped on the boards, *All life,* Hamlet said,
but that was centuries later, they are not characters but rather
actors, men who play their trade in front of an audience
or crowd, they believe in poetry, for instance, or love the
tragic boots, and comedy is not beyond them, their voices
are strong, and they are strong-muscled, and weave from
brute masculine animal to the delicate feminine stance in
a few lines, and a quick-change in the scene room, without
them there is only words, yes, but no action, no life in the
theatre, everything revolves about them, these two actors, one
playing the protagonist, the other the antagonist, sometimes
switching these roles, sometimes playing women or children
or old men, in from the hills, celebrities in the city Dionysia,
all Athens hails them, these practitioners of the fugitive, who
will be forgotten as quickly as they were lauded, leaving town
trailing an ox cart, they will find passage to Sicily, then Rome,
and it will take them centuries before they find England, and
even hundreds of more years before, arguing in an alehouse,
one decides to play Hamlet, while the other opts for Claudius.

ANTIGONE

Out in the desert there is an aerial view of a condor's glide through cloud-high air, and in the sand scorpions and vultures birl Polynices' unburied form. Antigone curses her king, and the studio bosses are worried. (Yes, she always was sassy, but never talked back to the directors like this.) It's suicide, her sister Ismene says, they're losing a hundred thousand a day working in this heat. Scorpions tread through her brother's fingers, giant ants gnaw his corpse, the condors land and fan out quickly, so that the vultures soon fly in. Antigone loves her brother more than Hollywood; she wishes to bury him in the dry desert ground before sunset.

Ophelia's Songs

First Song

The flowers, she said
To her little friend,
Are as soft as a mouse.

Let's play in a sandbox
Or make pie in my house;
You bring your toy fox.

Second Song

You are my clouds;
You are my sun.
You are my stars;
You are my love,
Oh Prince of Sunshine.

Mad about Hamlet

(sung to the tune of "Mellow Yellow")

I'm just mad about Hamlet
Hamlet's so mad about me
I'm just mad about Hamlet
He's mad about me

He calls me mad Ophelia
That's right
He calls me mad Ophelia
He calls out
Ophelia I want to feel ya
I want to feel ya
Right now
He calls me mad Ophelia
I want to feel ya
He calls me I want to
feel ya mad Ophelia
right now

HAMLET'S SONG

FIRST SONG

As I grow older
I think I am getting young
My mind responds to plays
With balletic agility
And the skin of my face
Instead of stretched jowlly
(The skull beneath the mask)
Gets tighter, showing
Every cavity of the hidden world
Its oddity and asymmetric
Bumps, curves, scars.

SECOND SONG

On a winter morning
With snow on the ground
And even the crows gone from
The ballfield across the street
I look in the freezing mirror
Of a bathroom before I shave
And my face is so tight
I feel the skin pulling across
The fractures of my nose

(The skull beneath the mask),
Creating a numb pain at my center.
I am as mortal as my own father,
As eternal as my father's ghost.

THE LOST SONNET: NUMBER 155

If you doubt my lover's Inventory,
I will pluck these items from The Rose:
First, a Rock upon which I will shout Fidelity;
Second, Three Tombes, one for my wife in repose,
Another for her faithless husband, and the third
For you, to whom I bequeath Two Steeples,
This Beacon, a Bay Tree, and for your little bird,
A Canopy, Small Altar, a Tree of Golden Apples.
Dear Mistress, this is madness owns me now.
I stalk The Rose as though a forgotten ghost;
My hands count the Inventory, looking for a cow,
Only to find a Chain of Dragons for my host.
       To you I give my Bedstead, home
          For Two Mossy Banks and the City of Rome.

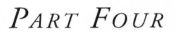

PART FOUR

THESPIS TO HIS CHORUS

"Let me walk from you as a friend and I promise the dithyramb will not suffer by this choric departure. If I offend, it is like Prometheus offending Zeus with fire. Let me be splendid in voice; you keep to dance-figures, and I, Hypokrates (he who answers) will not disobey Dionysos, but will answer back. Arion gave you poetic measure to make art of your ungulations. I offer the Gods ethos and breath. Pisistratos calls me to Athens to execute the dance, and it is there upon the earth-beaten floor I will step from you, perfect in memory, out loud, on the hoof, I will be Herakles, though I was born Thespis, and Liar! Liar! the politicians will call, but let them, for the people will love it and love me, for I will be Silenus and Hector in an unpainted linen masque, and I will be called an actor."

RÉSUMÉ

How was it that Hamlet was a young man, a preppie, as the director Andrei said, an adolescent, when the gravedigger said he had himself been thirty years the sexton, since King Hamlet deposed Fortinbras, since young Hamlet was born? And Yorick was dead twenty-three years, and Hamlet rode on his back when he was a boy. Alas, poor Yorick. Hamlet is thirty-something years old, beyond the age of rebellion, and this makes his inaction deeper and longer than was thought. Perhaps he needs anti-depressants. Are we to expect a manic swing? He was nearly a stone but for that searching mind; he was in his thirties, not married, not gainfully employed, his degree work still in process, still living off his mother and her new husband, still a student. Would you hire this man for even a low-paying summer job?

DRIVING

Like an actor who lost purpose, I drove through mountains, valleys, glens, there was no reason for this. My passion was you, this car, this destination, found on no maps, I had rehearsed it as a tryst, this rendezvous, us, together, alone, the wind hooted, the air was cold again, that was nothing compared to the purpose of this drive, to be together, motels came into my mind, a room of our own. It was a room of terrible decor in which we would see each other, perceive this moment, seconds, minutes, a few hours, what's that matter, to undress, to unfurl, to say these present-tense things, like the stage, a wonderful performance, something to quote, this was not to be missed, the throughlines, the storyboard, the purpose, oh the purpose was intense, insane, infinitely more wonderful than anything he had yet to imagine.

ALIAS THE ARCHANGEL

My grandmother called me Mickey O'Shay, and my mother said Michael, my father never called any of his children by their given names, our many voices interchangeable like mix-and-match apparel he now wears in his retirement village in Florida. Hey, Slick, my man, this dude on the street calls out, you happen to have a quarter you don't need? You better not go out tonight, buddy, if you want to see tomorrow, this gravelly voice on the telephone informs me. Who is this? What do you want? Click, he hangs up. I want to tell all that I am not named for my Uncle Mike, because I don't have an uncle by that name, nor am I named after Mike the Barber or Crazy Mike the bookie and loan shark, and no one ever called me Micheluzzo or Mikhail or Misha. A few old friends used to call me Miguel or Miguelito. I was named after the Archangel, his fiery sword brandished to smite Lucifer, the fallen angel, and how this mighty appellation is the commonest of all names. Still, I get telephone calls for Kevin the Bartender, Tough Ernie, Big Balls, and Mr. Nugget, and Queer Vinnie, none of whom I personally know, or maybe even want to know. Often I am called perfectly horrible names, and likewise I have been known to call others the same ones. I have been called in the night and in the daytime, darling, ogre, creep, son of a bitch, motherfucker, cocksucker, shit-for-brains, stupid jerk, dear, sir, mister, doctor. No one ever calls me Mickey anymore. Lately they have called me Hamlet.

AFTER HORSE

My play closed last night, not to raves and wows but the wild fury of that act of impersonation on the stage in quiet light and the audience's applause. It was a good show. The play was about a reunion of two friends after many years, their division having been Vietnam, how one went, the other stayed behind, and how they used to play basketball together, and were playing now, and the fact that that dirty little war ripped the souls out of a generation of us who cared to notice it was raging, oh it was raging, and it still does for some, it still rages in the body so many years after termination. Then, edgy, I went out the next day for a long walk with my future ex-wife down Broadway, and we stopped into Tower Records, buying Aretha, Taj, and for reasons which I didn't understand until this moment, a tape by Nina Simone. Who is she? my wife asks, a singer herself, and I explained how I used to go hear her at the Village Gate with my friend Paul Lee when we were kids, and before he went off to Vietnam, and I listened to the tape, and remembered how Paul and I listened to her records, her and Coltrane and Miles in his basement through that long summer on Long Island. The week Paul came back from 'Nam, we drank beers, but it was never the same, and we didn't speak again for ten years, it was at a brother's wedding, and I was thinking of him again, and then a couple days later, another brother calls me to say that Paul had died on that Monday. Agent Orange, the brother said, and he was thirty-eight years old, and ran a successful restaurant on the Island, and there was nothing left to do but listen to that tape of Nina Simone, and hope that the emptiness wouldn't last forever.

The Kingfisher

Perched high up in the loft of a pine, it lets out a fatigued, high and dry lunatic rattle. One hundred times the size of the ruby-throated hummingbird, it hovers before a dive, nonetheless like a giant hummingbird, and the breaking of the surface of the glassy lake water, and it is not unlike the hummingbird, though its wing-rattle sounds like a helicopter, shifting gears. This solitary thing's wings flap, bat-like, until it spies a ripple on the water, then it plunges—exclamation point, bullet—splash, it descends, from the world of sun into the muddy dark of the lake's bottom, suddenly an aquatic thing, and then it flies upward like a blue tracer, a bass in its bill, and back on its perch in its lofty tree, the king lets out another rattle, and it echoes over the lake and across the pine barrens....

DINNER

The fish is on the dish. Water is in the glasses. Silverware is on the table. Next to the fork. Next to the plate. Next to the spoon. Which is above the chair. There is a hair in the bowl. Remove it or leave the table. The carrots are in a bed of lettuce. Bread sticks out from a covered tray. You may begin to eat. Keep the napkin in your lap. Speak only when spoken to.

Pinhead News

This Zippy gives you weird dreams, and this pinhead must have weird dreams, yow! Maybe we are happy together. The government's secret agenda is all about tidy dick, yow! Call up W. C. Woods and tell him what you've discovered. Yikes! I wonder if he is home. And I used to think phlegm was the neatest product since detergent. If Zippy is happy, and I am happy, then we must be related. Yow! This is fun, like algebra and barf. Nuclear war must be like this. An idea: I'll drop an atomic bomb on Farmville, Virginia. My friend Bill Woods will get a kick out of that, and it should light a fire under his rump. There are no preservatives or artificial colorings in warheads. They must be good. They are good. And I am good. Yow! Me and Zippy, imagine the Brazilians creating a bossa nova from all this. Yow! Hey, let's lambada. Barring that, let's take a walk, I know a nearby McDonald's.

Pick a Number, One through Ten

We are drinking warm beers in the Wagon Wheels or the Eagle Tavern or the Silver Dollar, beer joints from years ago and my youth out on the Island, and nothing happens, nothing is happening, I am at the bar with my friend, Mr. Can of Beans, beers, and sometimes shots, Irish, but no broads, no nothing, only the old regulars, pot-bellied, balding, our age, for we are pot-bellied and balding, too, and my friend says, This is Number Ten, while this joker down the bar says that Bo Derek is Number Ten, not this place, but my friend says to me that Bo Derek is not Number Ten, she is a Ten, and that's a big difference, because you had to have been there, he says, to know what Number Ten is, himself a former Screamin' Eagle, a quiet man these days, like he says, "I'd rather be a lover than a fighter," and suddenly we feel so old, not toothless, we are old fools to be here, and the beer tastes flat, there isn't a woman for miles, and if this is Number One, maybe we forgot how to count like we did in the old days.

First Memory, Pure Fiction

In that first trimester, Mother grew out into her third pregnancy, and her two mickey-faced boys imped about in the rowhouse of a seedy Maryland town. First Germany fell, then Japan exploded atomically, Hiroshima, Nagasaki, until it was autumn, and leaves turned golden and red, only to fall to the ground. It snowed the night I was born in our nation's Capitol, another Navy brat delivered, and before the year was out, we had come home to Brooklyn, where all my brothers and sisters were born, except me. I was always weird, an older brother said, I had to be born in Washington. I think this is what they mean by post-modern. Years later, married, a child of my own, I stood in the middle of Tokyo, and I thought that because I was not born in Brooklyn, I was the strangest child, and how much of us forms in that first trimester.

FLAT ON MY BACK IN A BED IN NEW YORK CITY

What's worse than teeth or feet is not a shrew, but this ache in my back, low-down and mean, it conjures itself by spasms ripping muscle, two days now I have not walked. What's worse than being out of work four months, bills piling up, the building going co-op and the landlord a carpetbagger, is this lower back, this goddamn back, this lumbar ache. Meanwhile, it is spring in the city, robins in the trees, the cherry blossoms out, the dogwood wild on the islands of upper Broadway, a gentle rain washes over everything, including my unwalkable ache. The only real consolation is a book of poems, and a particular one by James Wright called "Lying in a Hammock at William Duffy's Farm in Pine Island, Minnesota," and I read this poem whenever I am down. It ends: "I have wasted my life." God, do I know what he means. I have done nothing but strive to overcome my childhood, only to find out that I am my childhood, and cannot escape it. I have tried to do esteemable things, only to wind up on the boards, an actor, a dissembler, a performer, playing Hamlet to an art-house audience. A woman, walking down the street the other day, wore a T-shirt that said *It Is Never Too Late to Have a Happy Childhood.* I wanted to bet her on that one. Then my aching back seized up, and I turned, I tried to turn, I was unable to turn at all, and so lay there, lay there and thought of lying in a hammock. It is there that I would contemplate how I played Hamlet.

This Is Her Life

In her habit of one glass leading to another down a corridor of dim lights and flattened jukebox music—Tony Bennett and the Clancy Brothers two of her favorites—my godmother's only friend was herself, and also her worst enemy, her red hair flamed, makeup ten years behind the time, her idea of fashion was a duck's ass haircut and pegged pants, though her sometimes lover (a token clerk for the Transit Authority) only wore drab suits, faded white shirts, his hands trembling for another drink. Her hair was bobbed in the front, glued down with sprays, odors of tobacco and alcohol her only cologne, her routine was of drinks and music, drinks and ladies room, drinks and saying goodnight to the bartender, getting her through day to day or until tomorrow, up early for a job at the lingerie shop on Pitkin Avenue in Brownsville in Brooklyn where she sold crossover bras, cotton undies, and panty hose, she smoked unfiltered Pall Malls, read her *Daily News,* coughed and cursed like a truck driver and more easily than a dock boss, "These fucking newcomers got their nerve, these dew-drop candyassed marginal marauders, these cantankerous indigents with their weird ingredients in all their food, these harbingers of the next wave of immigration, these flags at sunrise waving surrender," she declared upon being robbed, tied up and punched in the face. Every ache in her body said, "I'll take you home again, Kathleen," and this is your life, this is your life, "only watch what I do the next time the bastards think they're going to rip me off!" and when they did, she beat the shit out of them, and then reeled home drunk on the streets of East New York, where so many of my own nightmares and dreams originated, that phantom landscape of turn-of-the-century tenements and row houses, that rookery, the long streets and the shadowless days, the roar of the subway's elevated tracks a few blocks over.

R & R

My first R & R was in Casablanca, a real deadbeat sort of town, and then the ship went on to Spain, I lost my cherry in a Palma de Majorca whorehouse in Chinatown, the Kansas Bar, it was called, and from there it was all rock and roll, I remember my first trip to Korea back in the seventies, no cherry anymore, I drove out of Seoul in a Mercedes, digging the rice fields, going up to Panmunjom, what a motherfucker that was, and the heat that summer was another kind of motherfucker, I played golf with an orange ball one winter, my brothers-in-law out to show me a good time, what I know about Asia has to do with what I know about anything, and I don't know a thing, still as cherry as that kid in Casablanca, looking for opium and theatrical acts which included women and donkeys.

BODY BUILDING

Their ideal was perfection, the human form, the Greeks, and so built temples like the body itself, lines and curves, struts and cavities. In this imperfect world, let me propose that our bodies are a kind of architecture, and if I say your thigh is like a marmoreal column, build it. Make of roundness like rotunda the sweet milk of love, and if your eyes are like windows, light a lamp inside your skull, for by morning, all this is gone. At my bath, I shower, naked, singing made-up arias from imaginary operas never performed in Italy, and without perfection of voice I present my imperfect architecture. There is more to the curve of a belly in heat than any altar built to Aphrodite, and maybe less. Still, build relationships, make the most of what is given. I have often thought, in an age of contraception, there is no longer the onus that was given Oedipus, and like the Greek gods themselves, we make love as we please. Brother and sister dance in shadows of such architecture, neither classical nor quite modern, the urge is toward the sky so blue, nothing like heaven enters it.

LEAR AT COLONNUS

Like birdsong, my sometime daughter calls with her injunctives without words, her morning face smeared with cottage cheese and marmalade. Dawn broke to her crying. She needs ministrations and demands of us attention, love, understanding. My daughter of blackberry eyes and chestnut hair calls across two worlds. Omma! she cries, and when that does not succeed, Mommy! Mommy! But who should show up is this man, her father, though she has no name for him in either his language or her mother's, but she is learning. He speaks calmly, at least, and tells her that her name means blackberry or the land of leprechauns, and so much guile goes into her expression, so much tender understanding of my place as though it were her removing my soggy diaper, and not the reverse, salving the red buttock, or her placing socks on cold feet or removing cheese from her blackberry eyes, I call daughter, daughter, as though I were Oedipus at Colonnus or Lear with his kingdom divided, and only one good, misunderstood sometime daughter left, sitting on my throne of monkey hides. Where is my fool? He is in the mirror, nuncle, she says, he is you and you is he.

PISISTRATOS

Like Odysseus, he faked his wounds and demanded club-bearers to avenge Athens, turning instead upon Athens but was driven out. Like Thespis he learned to lie and, beaten into the hills, return with a whore disguised as their goddess Athena. Beaten once again, he brooded on the Akropolis, and like a trickster, advanced a sneak attack. All Athens was his to rule, and so he gave them Dionysos in the form of the chorus and his friend Thespis. Not a bad deal, if you were an Athenian.

The Green Room

Dionysos lay on a couch with Ariadne. And to his right,
Eros. And to his left, a satyr. Below, the poet spoke with an
Oriental king. A maiden, Herakles, Silenus in panther pelt.
The winning play is to be announced. The choregos paces.
Actors take off masques. The protagonist dances. They were
given five votes. Go find the drunken playwright. Their play
has won a wreath.

O'Shaughnessy's Notebook

"Hamlet—the play about murder and revenge—but the character is about a person of sensuality, uncertainty, sensibility, intelligence, and intellectual fire...."

THE BRITCHES HAMLET DREAM

Like the rivers and mountains without end, when she came forward, not as Ophelia but as Hamlet, I went for her, searching through the saddle of hills, up ravines in rock crevices, slipping slipping all the time, though telling myself, This is the way to find it, and it was one way to find her, cutting through crag and foggy night, through densities, I came into a clearing and went along the hedgerow, wondering where was her cottage and where she might be at this time of day, the sun low in the sky with autumn, birds raced across the horizon, beating wings to the south, and the truth was I enjoyed this kind of searching, because I promised myself she would be across the next rise, around a new bend in the river, foraging for meals, breaking the high grass, deeper into the woods I wandered. This was not Ophelia anymore, for she had none of her sadness, none of her madness, or any of the traditional earmarks of that forlorn, ghostly girl. She was like a bright light ahead, the first light that cut through the high, dense canopy, and I knew she was up ahead, only a few more feet, deeper into the haze, I called her name several times, I spoke with her in my nights, I called to her far away and so near, Hamlet, Hamlet, Hamlet....

ORESTES

When they came back from Iraq and Afghanistan, there were some who said these lives were like Agamemnon, the great warrior home for his own killing. But he had thought of them as Orestes, the prodigal son, come home to avenge the family name. Orestes is the one who must perform the terrible deed which no one else is willing to do. The Big O is the one who thinks and acts. Orestes needs his Apollo to ward off the Furies. Every person who fought in Iraq or Afghanistan knows about the Furies. He was thinking about this the other night, drinking beer with two friends who were veterans. He looked at them and realized that both of them created justice in his time. They drank to that and some other things. Then they went home; and he went home. The Furies were amenable; they had become house-spirits, rooted in the hearth. He shouted their names across the night street on Broadway. Oh, you Eumenides, you wild-haired girls! I am not going to strafe your villages anymore.

MISE EN SCÈNE

The cook pens his poems in the pantry. A policeman walks down Broadway, whistling an aria from Puccini's *Turandot*. Some high wire aerialists come down to earth at the steps of the Metropolitan, drinking mineral water and discussing bones. The everyday is not a separate reality from the extraordinary. The mailman says, Imagination pretends, and then we send it on holiday. Ah, Rose Selavy, here is your letter from the dead poet in Paris that you wrote to a lifetime ago. Achtung! Rose shouts. Monks dream of crucifixions, their own and their master's. Duelists speak of sharp swords after exchanging sharp words. The milk maiden's breasts are so swollen and large that she creates the illusion that all milk comes from her fountains. In new places of excitement the trumpeter pauses, jotting down ideas in her notebook. A florist speaks floridly of trysts on rocky shores. Two secretaries share the intimacies of Matisse's deeper secrets on a park bench. Like unlit attractions to oblivion, the homeless are only quaint and/or putting us on, if our homes are perpetually heated, food always on the table nightly, from youth until this morbid now. These are not so much bleak opposites as exigencies of termination, the extremities of midnight, the proclivities of the dawn. A mouse catcher scurries off to work in the shadowless corners before sun up, and a car swirls in the snowdrifts. Ten businessmen drink coffee on the steps of Carnegie Hall, each presuming to have nothing in common with the other. The maestro observes these details and jots them down, not for a canvas but a scenario he plans to videotape later in the month if the grant he applied for comes through. These proclivities of dawn like the extremities of midnight are exigencies of termination, not so much bleak opposites as unlit attractions of oblivion, the ones finding themselves in new places of excitement. Or maybe it is just another example of the imagination pretending to be a separate reality from the quotidian, when the everyday is really the mind at its very best. Lawyers argue these points into a fine dust. I am the only one who writes it down with broken pens on old headline pages, using a flashlight to distinguish one line from another, the edges of the page from the middle, the nouns from the verbs, the syllables, count them, as they dance under the halogen arc created by the light itself attached to two batteries, the hand getting printer's ink on the sleeve of the chambray shirt, as the leaking pen annihilates all these distinctions.

THE GLASS OF FASHION (2)

Here is to impossible things like weddings, like love, and to people who make art like people in the neighborhood take book, effortlessly, with care, and great digression. I am talking about impossible things, like two people coming together, of words and the dance, and the improbable, like the World Trade Center precarious as a domino about to fall, we fall in love, we love, it's as simple as the theme song from *The Godfather,* or a roomful of theatre people with stemmed glasses (plastic cups will do), toasting the long life of a playwright, a dancer, our friends, these people who have come together, not in June, but September when the heat breaks and the city nights are cool because they are cool and hot, they have the heat to marry, as in movies, like mysteries or thrillers, the climate demands voodoo turning into rock & roll as evening progresses past midnight, and the tugboats sounding on the Hudson blocks away, and the World Trade Center looks as though it might topple down like a domino. Here is to two people—I won't romanticize it because I am talking about two lives—this oneness is unbelievable, is wonderful, and we know it is tough, is impossible, is possible but still impossible, or is impossible but possible, like those towers in the background, twin towers....

Sur la Route

I'm walking down the highway where they are working on the highway, it's a hot sort of day and I'm on my way to work down the highway on this sort of day which is hot and humid, I'm not timid when I say hello to the men on the highway because they are working and I am going to work, I say, Hi, they say, What's happening, it is an ordinary day except that the highway is full of heat bubble twists, the drifters drink wine at the roadway intersection, all of us dreaming of intercourse, more than interstate commerce, I know, I say to myself, I was working on the highway, once going down a highway to work like I am going now, only I was working for the highway, and now I am using the highway, it's that sort of day....

The Point Is

Down George IV, high off a show down on Market Street at Buster Brown's next to the railroad station, I went up an alley to High Street (the Royal Mile), and stepped into a gallery, prints and postcards, cards and memorabilia of Scotland, I bought a print, an Asian cup and pens in it, a flower, a yellow daffodil, oh the women in espadrilles, and the España company, the street theatre, the whole goddamn fringe was acting, and these actors were acting out, and the others out on the street were out looking for actors, and I (the writer) was going to Greyfriars Bobby for a pint, the point being I was drunk as a skunk, I was carousing in midafternoon in Edinburgh. I was no longer Hamlet. I was Cornelius Michael O'Shaughnessy, playwright, here at the Edinburgh Fringe Festival with my play.

Souvenir

This is the first of many flowers I will send to redheaded women in this town, but only the first of many flowers. Consider this batch of flowers done, they are sent.

First Will and Testament

When there was no more paper but this one white sheet, I had to think and think what or how to write, my life stops and begins here, and when the words would not stop because they had a life not always my own, I stepped back to watch them form and turn, breaking out of themselves like a migration of ducks or a convention of salesmen, I had only a few more beats left before the page extinguished, and perhaps instead of silence I would talk, make friends, be a good man, a citizen, or maybe I would act like a father, like a husband, and learn to cook pasta right, clean rooms spotlessly, and go about my work without complaint, it is not the drink per se, I want to tell her, I was a moody son of a bitch as a child and probably early on in this life, dropped on my head, I got the idea to become an actor, what a joke, but I was known also for my sense of humor, my fits of strength, and I was never strong, yet I happened to be a good fighter, and now that I conclude I say that I said this poorly, missing the major points, exaggerating the lesser ones, that's me too, so what else is new?

COMEDY

Polonius is the father and fool;
His smug pronouncements are so laughable,
It is hard to take them seriously,
About his "to thine own self be true," and

Other such malarkey, it's a wonder
That he seemed to last as long as he did,
Until Hamlet caught some movements behind
The arras and stabbed through the cloth into

Polonius' heart, and even then he
Wasn't so much tragic as ridiculous,
Not a figure of concerned sympathy,
As he was patriarchal annoyance.

And still Ophelia loved him, yet Hamlet—
While others honored the dead—showed contempt.

PART FIVE

THE GRAVEDIGGERS

Goodman, delver, goddamn the night these graves filled with stones and skulls. Ophelia dances no more. Yorick is no more than the jawbone of an ass. I can see the skull beneath Hamlet's face.

Rice Malt Hops

When the pleasure was gone from it, she saw the drink only as disease, but that didn't stop her from drinking it one more time, one more round, bartender, set up the house, and while you're at it, refill my endless cup, or better yet, forget the glass and hand me a long-neck bottle I'll slug from, for the road, to your health, for old times, the good old days, for days gone by, the dead and gone, for your children, wife, your new dog, for bygones and forget-me-nots, whatshisname, to the champagne under the willows, monkey-face, to Maxwell Bodenheim, Harry Kemp, the Ravenswood Poetry Society, to Jack Kerouac, James Joyce, to the nameless derelicts in the Whale's Inn off Houston Street on the Bowery, the old gang at Max's, St. Adrian, the Tin Palace, to the new ones uptown, the mailman, let's drink to the mailman and his route, the pipefitter down the bar, to that old whore in her cups who drinks during Happy Hour at the same old seat by the dirty windows—wait a minute you son of a bitch, that's me in the mirror behind the bar, you bastard—what? no more for me, you say, what do ya mean by that, friend, I'm your friend, we are old buddies, old buddy, well, fuck you, too, I never liked you anyhow, fuck you, your wife and children, and fuck your dog, too, because I never liked your family and I liked your dog even less, and besides that, I don't have to drink here anymore, there are a lotta places that want to serve me and want my company, so fuck your ugly wisecracking face, buddy, my bully boy, my old fucking friend, fuck you and where you come from, where you eat and breathe, fuck everything about you, you two-timing dickhead, you creep, you cheat, you five-and-dime, nickel-ante, dime-a-dance, bargain-basement excuse for a bartender, all right, all right, all right already, I'm leaving, don't push, get your stinkin' hands off of me....

"Do you know who I am?"

"Hamlet," the bartender said.

"That's right," I answered. "I'm Hamlet. I was Hamlet. Now I'm no longer him. I'm O'Shaughnessy. You remember me. I used to drink here quite a bit."

"I don't often say this to a customer, buddy," the bartender said. "But have you ever thought of getting sober? This city is filled with drunken Hamlets and would-be Hamlets and people who played Hamlet and even Hamlet himself."

SONNET SONG

My mistress is a tempest in camera, and on camera she purrs like a tiger. Oh, tender one, your tender loins so tasty, fitting into my groin. If I give you heat and trust, if you offer me wetness and lust. What is the gender of the beast with two backs at this nocturnal feast? After that night we became a pair. We sat on the bedsheet, eating a pear. Love, if only I thought of it—two more lines make this a sonnet. But I lack, what a poet called formal invention, the rigorous formality of poetry; I think he meant that I write prose, that this is prose, and it's true. I do I do I do.

DOCKSIDE SOLILOQUY

They were not whiskey-breathed men, my father and his friends, they came home sodden from work, and with the sweet-sour scent of draught beer. Before the sun rose, they were off to work a long shift on the docks, then hanging in there late for overtime. On vacations, we were allowed to come along, usually when an ocean liner was in port, get a free lunch, tour the ship, then come home tired, and bickering. The longshoremen would come over, slapping you with a big, friendly hand, and of me, "Hey, he looksa 'talian!" Most of the waterfront is gone now, and the wharf rats have swum to Jersey, the longshoremen, Customs inspectors, shipping company people, they've retired to Florida or work at the airport. The rough dockside bars are gay hangouts now, the Westside Highway scrapped, the piers empty. I say this with the sweet-sour scent of beer on my breath, and cigarettes, my daughter at my side, holding my hand. I say it with the memory of the sweet-sour scent of beer on my breath and on the air, and my daughter grown up and the docks empty. I say it without cigarettes now, without the sweet-sour breath, my father in a nursing home in Florida, retired and sundowning at night in the ward for demented old men who drank themselves out of a mind. I sing this for my lost father, long dead and gone, a man from another era. This is Hamlet talking to you, and I'm driving a taxicab.

Pig Latin

When Catulle mounts her like a dog, she calls him a dog, but when he comes on her after the legs are spread, taking in the sun, she calls him her love. This suggests that there is a proper way to do everything, and the right time of day in which to get it done. His lover asks him to come by in the early morning hours.

How They Die

They die mostly by stabbing, though some just
Disappear, while others are beheaded
Or drown, drop dead instantly of fright or
Fatigue (read here lethargy or despair),
There are those, like Oedipus, who are not
Killed but annihilated by blindness,
Rendered into a cipher by circum-
Stance or some other intractable stance,
And there are those who are ripped apart by
A mob (think of the Bacchae, for instance),
Or those who are simply wasted by life,
Pursued by a bear, smothered by a loved
One's pillow, hung, kept from sleep by endless
Depredations, by being forced to stay
Awake indefinitely until they
Also expire, not from life or war, but
From a lack of rest, dreamless in their last
Hours, pleading for just a little nod out
Under the sycamore tree (a plane tree
By another name), some are thrown down wells
Or out of high-floor windows, some are doused
In rivers or oceans, whipped and stretched out,
Some are thrown away as if they are just

Rubbish, some die by asphyxiation,
Others eat so little that they dissolve
Before our eyes, disappearing one ounce
At a time or get chopped up and cooked in
A stew that is served to their family
Members, as in the house of Atreus,
Some die of indigestion, others by
Indiscretions and humiliations,
By public hanging or private parties
To their suicides, and like crows baked in
A pie, some die from the intense heat, while
Others die of the cold, stripped of blankets,
The radiator busted, some others
Die of sorrow or loneliness, or die
Ineluctably by being ground down
To a fine salt, laughing or crying, they
Die, disturbed, resentful, even grateful,
Some by as dull a method as butter
Knife, and others falling on their own sword,
And there are those who die of love and grief,
Criminals breaking down their doors, some who
Die peacefully in their sleep, who conjure
A suite of music to drift forever
Off and away, poems being whispered

In their slowly-turning-to-stone old ears,
Or their sight goes away, their smell, their taste,
Or like Molly in *Happy Days,* being
Buried alive in a mound of dirt, some
Are dismembered, limb from limb, like chicken
Meat pulled from the bones, some are remembered,
Others are forgotten as soon as they
Leave the mortal coil, some are set on fire,
Some are blown to smithereens, gassed or smoked,
They close their eyes as if to sleep, and die
In their favorite reading chair in the
Living room, among family who seem
To remain among the quick, even as
Others go out to walk the dog and then
Never return, at least not alive, they
Should be memorialized for their wit
And humor, their book collections, paintings
They owned or even ones they painted in
The twilight years of their lives, lean works of
Incredible inspiration, though a
Reminder the reaper, grim or simply
Otherwise, is waiting for you and me
On even our best days, though generally
We die on what is probably our worst

Day, yet it could also have been our best,
And what differentiated it from
All the other days of our lives, is how
It is truncated, a day like any
Other day in our lives, only shorter.

CELTIC FLOWERS

Joyce said redheaded women buck like goats, only I saw no goats in Scotland (this was not Ireland) to verify the sage's wisdoms, I would say that there are no redheads like the bird of Bennets, to be more exact I cannot be, she was not even Celt but Rooskie, or something like that, and if she bucked, it was not I to verify, being a tourist in this town, I had a play going up, and down, and occasionally the actors stepped into this pub for a pint of lager or something heavy, or a single malt liquor of which I am not versed. I thought of Yeats' red rose, but again I should have read my Bobby Burns, wasn't it he who invented the word *fuck?* This has nothing to do with flowers except as I write this down I recall Japanese clusters—chrysanthemums, other things, it was late, I was drunk, God forgive me....

Further Autobiographical Scribble

I'm going to England tomorrow, having never been there before, I'm looking forward to this trip, and Scotland, my play being done, I wrote this play, and now it is done. The actor C. Michael O'Shaughnessy has become a writer. I lived downtown for seven years, I wrote in the biographical note, and then lived uptown for eleven years, making a grand total of eighteen years on the island of Manhattan; I got married, had a kid, found a job to support everyone. I went off to sea, I wrote, when I was a teenager, like so many other men in my family, my uncle died at sea on a tanker off the coast of southern Korea, near the port of Pusan, he was thrown overboard. I lived out on Long Island, I went on, when I was still a kid, the cows were down the road, the roadside vegetable stands, the truck farms, I played basketball until dark every day. I spent my formative years in East New York, I played stoop ball on my Irish grandmother's stoop with the Spalding, the Spaldeen. I was not born in Brooklyn, I said, like everyone else in my family, my brothers and sisters, my mother, her mother, her father, his father, and so on. But then I was told that I didn't need the biographical note, the company manager said, writers aren't that important in show business, she informed me.

HROSWITHA OF GANDERSHEIM

It was before the invention of firebreeding monsters, before it cost five pence to keep the world on fire and the damned stewed in Hellmouth of Seventeen Machines at the gaping hole of Asto or Infernus across from the House of the Sun, the House of the Eternally Heavenly Father and the Seven Angels. You lit the lamp on the Dark Ages; you invented the science of the blush. Your Maria was raped, and ran to the brothel in shame. You witnessed in your books, the rape of three virgins by Roman generals. Met pimps, whores, sponges, cooks which Terence bequeathed the millennium—the gift of the first black poet to a secret nymph in her blackened robes. Translate! Adapt! Redact! Cull! Delete! Ah! I picture you as pink as you are fat, a cherubic Reubens, working this Carthaginian's pagan craft to your holy ends.

The Dancer

At the end-point, she was let go to the changing room for dry clothes, and salt-sweat hung on to her body, and she peeled off her leotards, her tights, she was now cool all over as though she were the air she wanted to walk naked through and into the streets of the suburbs, naked as the day she came into the world, and as she would go from it that cool night. But then she dressed into jeans and shoes and a T-shirt, and so drove home. Her boyfriend would be by in a little while, and they planned to go shopping at the mall and then catch a late movie at the cinemaplex down the road.

The Person I Was

The old man said: The person I was will always be drunk, the one I am now has the choice not to be the person I was, but the person I am and the one I was are both drunks, only now I choose not to drink, day by day, one day at a time, and the other guy, the person I used to be, is still out there doing his pushups—his press-ups, we used to call them in England—slugging down beers, ready for the next chug-a-lug contest. Then he laughed and said: Forget whatever it was I said. I'm still the same old full-of-shit bastard I was, drunk or sober.

HELEN IN STRATFORD

And here comes Helen, who let sail those ships.... Oh, Helen, your eyes are so swollen with intelligence and sensuality and the sunlight of North Africa, nights in Egypt spent on a divan by the window, wondering when Agamemnon might arrive full of his male ego and rage to make war on these people of sand and desert mirages that they mistake for visions. I will not go to her, he said, softly. I will go back to my book. Or I will fall asleep, dreaming of the city, and my plans for life once I get back there. I'll write, read, think, sleep, and I'll dream.

DAY BY DAY BY DAY

Pound said day by day, make it new. Actually, it was Tching, and he didn't say it, he wrote it on his bathtub. Dorothy Day ran the Catholic Worker off the Bowery. I once heard Anita O'Day sing "Honeysuckle Rose" and "My Funny Valentine" simultaneously at the bar of the Half-Note when it was on Hudson at Spring Streets. One of my favorite poems is by Frank O'Hara called "The Day Lady Died." Abner Doubleday is another story. I heard he could pitch and chew gum simultaneously. One day I woke and got up, the fact being that for a time I woke but could not get up and out of bed. I wasn't sick, but crazy. It had nothing to do with being lazy. I was feeling blue, if you will. That turned into a funk, then I freaked, which turned into a rage gone sour. Call it depression at the eleventh hour. I could not face another day. Now I take it one day at a time, day by day. O Anita, Dorothy, Ez, Frank, and Abner, each day I take it that way.

Flat-Penny Days

The trick was to play hooky, though it was done after school, too. My brothers stole horses from the Valentine estate, riding them in the pasture until a stable-hand caught them, chasing them as far as Hillside Avenue. There, bored, they laid down pennies on the tracks, anticipating the mid-afternoon train to Oyster Bay. This one time, neither stealing rides on horses nor playing hooky from school, it was summer and the air thick with humidity, a gray day in August when nothing moved in the still air. It was a friend's younger brother who laid down his pennies before the train arrived, hoping to retrieve a squashed, flat, long and irregularly shaped object of copper, our heads filled with stories of how trains were derailed by such tricks by young children such as ourselves, neither delinquents nor truants nor psychos, but with nothing to do, nowhere to go, nothing in our heads, time on our hands, and nothing to say to each other, we hung around the tracks, putting pennies out to be squashed by the train coming from Mineola on its way to Oyster Bay. My friend's brother was a wiseguy, always full of mischief, and when he would not unglue himself from the rail, we thought he was playing with us, trying to give everyone a scare, playing chicky with the train's engineer who tooted his whistle, but too late. Several yards from his fractured and dismembered body was the good, smooth, copper flat penny, even if it was a lot harder trying to piece together the body parts of my friend's kid brother, though one of my friends found part of his finger not far from where the penny was located. I think it rained the next day, so no one went down to the tracks, and after that school began, and, besides, I wasn't really there or I probably could not have written this down, but heard it when I returned to school after summer, and someone asked if I remembered Johnny's little brother Chris, yeah, I said, well, the other kid said, you heard what happened to him down at the tracks, didn't you?

DEAR LANDLORD

The note from the landlord read: prior to gaining entry to the building be sure that there is no one (stranger) near you.

LENTILS

Four garlic cloves a carrot some celery olive oil 5 cups of water
thyme rosemary bay leaf mushrooms an onion or two and of
course the lentils cook for two hours read a book or write a
long letter eat when ready enjoy.

The Drifters

Sunday night dance: pink shirt charcoal gray slacks black shoes black tie. Boys on one side girls on the other until an hour into it, then they sing: "Everything I want I have...." This tragic moment, so indifferent and so old lasts only a moment and is gone. Until I kissed you. Fouler than Thunderbird. Nothing in this summer night. They sing. "Everything I want I have...."

SELF-HELP

He told me, both of us on the flight deck of the rehab, that when his father was drunk on rum, the old man lay snoring on his bed upstairs. The patient said, "I placed a burning cigarette between his dark fingers and whispered, 'die, motherfucker,' and I poured kerosene on his mattress, lit it, and went back to my room, where I pretended to sleep, listening to the flames crackle, smelling the smoke. Burn, baby, burn, I sang. But he came to just before the flames consumed his workingman's body; he woke me and the other children, rushing us into the streets of St. Albans, Queens, New York, where we all watched the fire lick through the upper rooms of our mortgaged house. Father asked if I was all right. 'I'm all right,' I said, but it was shortly after that that I left home and joined the Marines."

THE HUMMINGBIRD

A spade is, like, a spade, ain't no either or about it, this shuffle aren't no shovel—no ifs about it, and if there are: dirt to dirt, dust to dust, ashes to—merrily we stroll along. Hey, let's boogie! Ain't no ands or buts about it, as if, and or, i.e., I got feet not wings, and this sparkle is no sparrow, the choices, the choices, a sparrow ain't no hummingbird, and I'll love you forever, until this dance is danced out, a man, a woman, Amen. No, no, not again. Look! Up in the sky! It's a bird, it's a hummingbird....

AN EXTRAORDINARY DAY
IN NEW HAVEN

In late afternoon I walk down Prospect Street—Divinity
School, the abandoned Culinary Institute mansion, Farnam
Gardens with its Chinese trees—I savor my thoughts, their
rhythm works with my stride, there are questions about
whether to drink coffee with Mark, and bullshit of Sophocles
and Chekhov, or head on to York Street, it's Friday, life well
with wife and child, and nothing to do until evening when
we see *Man Is Man,* I content myself with the few sparrows
out, say hello to friends waiting for a bus, when it strikes me
that I'm too old to be here, I might be crossing swords with
America, or drinking with friends in New York, and instead
I am bound for the Gypsy bar for shop talk with Arthur
or John, if they stayed on this evening, or I stop into the
bookstore, an idea for a play in my head, no ideas, there is
a poem somewhere, I search the shelves, and then it is gone,
one by another man, another set of circumstances, but this
city, ah but I admire him as I grow older, and my grandfather
was from the Cliffs of Moher (really more inland in Clare),
and now I must rush, because my friends are leaving shortly,
there is a new play opening tonight....

Oxford Street Blues

A wonderful street person on Oxford, selling hot perfume: "I am not going to lie to you, this merchandise is hot, is how come I can sell it so cheap." He sits on the sidewalk on a box, is surrounded with opened boxes of perfume which he liberally sprays into the air, on the arms of passersby, he snaps a magazine to his thigh, and shows us pictures of the royal family, then flaps to the last page, an ad for one of the perfumes, CK, he is selling, and before you can see the price, he says, "it cost thirty pounds in one of these fancy department stores, but I'm going to give it to you for ten pounds, but...." not only that, ladies and gentlemen, he is going to throw in a bottle of Chanel, and not only that, sirs and madames, he will throw in a bottle of Polo, and lastly, "I am going to give you this bottle of Pierre Cardin perfume, not ten pounds each, not thirty pounds for one bottle, but ten pounds for all four. But," he says, "I ain't got all day. If the police come from there, me and my associate are going in the opposite direction." He snaps the magazine on his thigh, he bags four bottles for a customer, and another, and still a third and a fourth.

LONDON

I walk down to Regent Street where I watch the buses careen by: Hackney Wick, Tooting Mitre, the street barkers' rhythms filling the air.

Language Lesson

The actors and I trained from Edinburgh to London after several weeks of doing my play at the Festival Fringe. I was thinking, daydreaming really, on the train, packed in like sardines, we were, and all of us with no sleep, our eyes were red, our heads were fuzzy, I kept thinking how I was in a foreign land. It was not language per se, but then it was language. We all spoke English, but each of us spoke it in our own way. Up north it had its Celtic rhythms, to the west the Irish did their justice to it, this English language, and the British themselves always spoke as though they had invented this tongue, which they had. So often I had heard that Americans butcher the mother tongue, and I had gotten tired of hearing this said. "We speak with the invention of Shakespeare," I answered. "We are not bothered with rules or by mere convention." But I was sipping a can of beer to batten down the pulsing ache in my head. I held a tall lager can in my shaky hand. On the beer can it read: "Best before see end of can." I read it several times, figuring I had short-circuited my brain, that I could no longer read English. Here were the inventors of the language. We crossed from Scotland into England on British Railways. Best before see end of can. Still so much to learn about this mother tongue, I thought. We Americans with our barbaric tongue, our yawp, I thought. Best before, it read, and without a bridge or break, it continued, see end of can. All right, I thought, I will.

Morning

I am going east but I am not going East. Are you going South, I am going south? But then I am going east and I am afraid that you are going away to the west or somewhere. O how I want to talk, but maybe talk is not all. How I want to engage you in this dialogue of spirits. Morning is a lovely time of day for this kind of dialogue. Spirits come and go and, like myself, who also comes and goes, I go. The moon went down, the sun was up, I was up, I was going some place, I was gone; I remember this last look on your face, so question marked, so savory and intricate, with no answers, only a face with questions. How I love mornings like this....

The Terrier

Maybe it's my nostalgia, but I see her now out walking the dog as the sun cuts over the street and sinks into the river. Her face is full of openness and intelligence, and I'll bet everyone tells her how cute she is. It is not a cute face, though. Something livelier than that lives in her cheekbones. There are days when I see her with that wonderfully stiff-legged dog, and both of them seem possessed of great fire, but maybe all terriers have that fire, and so their owners, too. I used to walk my little bullterrier up and down this block years ago, and once in a while I miss that crazy little dog. One hot summer's night I saw her in the local cafe, drinking pitchers of wine with her friends, they were drunk and laughing, having a good time. Near closing, I bumped into her group, going out the door, and talked to them. But that was so long ago, and I haven't even seen the woman with the terrier on this street in a long time. I wonder why I think about all of this, and I tell myself, maybe it's nostalgia. Maybe I need to get back to doing auditions again.

HAMLET'S ADVICE TO THE PLAYERS

O'Shaughnessy sat in the Spanish café on upper Broadway, back in Manhattan, back to his home on the Upper West Side, in Morningside Heights. He drank his *café con leche,* dreaming of playing other Hamlets, this one he had played over and done. His own four boards and a passion took him from New York to New Haven, from Edinburgh to London, and then back again, like the riverrun, the Cathedral of Saint John the Divine up the block, up the street, around the corner, verging into Harlem. He could walk over to the Hungarian Pastry Shop and have another coffee, but it would not taste as good as this Spanish coffee. Hamlet the prism. Hamlet the point that is nowhere and everywhere. Hamlet the play that pissed off Mr. Eliot, old Possum. Hamlet the play that intrigued James Joyce. The play that drew out the genius of O'Shaughnessy's last director. Four boards and a passion. A piece of linoleum and an idea. Some floor boards and compassion. To be, to be, to become, to come, to be. He might order a ham omelet. He just might. Be natural. Be present. Be there. Just being was probably the most spiritual thing anyone could do, actor or otherwise. So he sat there, O'Shaughnessy did, and he thought. If I don't drink today, he thought, that will be another action. Perhaps he thought better than he acted, which in turn made him a good Hamlet, if not blond-haired, if not thirty-three years old, Hamlet and Jesus. O'Shaughnessy was a bit longer in the tooth than they were. But he was still a young enough man. He had his youth, his passions, which remained with the theatre, reading and writing, and thinking, always thinking, perhaps the one Germanic piece of the puzzle, his passion for that, these ideas in pure form, free-floating, free of anxiety, as shapely as abstract paintings, as clean-lined as a drawing by Matisse. Perhaps he ought to think of playing Oedipus, of playing, one day at least, the old King Lear. He thought of acting on the boards as opposed to taking parts in movies to pay the rent. He thought of acting again. The idea of theatre intrigued him still. To be, to be, drinking *café con leche* up a tree. Ophelia would be as beautiful as the Spanish waitresses in this café, as sexy and as fiery, as dark and mysterious, her eyes as electric as Maria's were, her café con leche complexion, her instinct to be. O'Shaughnessy thought and thought at that table in front of his cup of coffee, back in his old neighborhood, back in Morningside Heights. I am the glass of fashion, he thought.

TAKING DICTATION FROM ANGELS

Some prefer to think
That they are the glass of
Their own fashion.

They would have you believe
That their imaginations sprout
From inside themselves *ex nihilo.*

But I recall the poet saying,
When asked how he wrote,
That he took dictation from angels.

Always Number Five

If it is mid-morning, the rush-hour ended, and I find myself near Lincoln Center or Columbus Circle, I hop on the Number Five bus instead of taking the usual M104 up Broadway and home, I go more leisurely to 72nd Street, left at Verdi Square, and over to Riverside Drive, and then uptown, and take in the park on the left and the grand curve of buildings on this always windy street, recalling a time two decades earlier when a British two-decker bus used to go along this route, and I'd stare in the second-story windows, watching how life was lived at those addresses, the inhabitants always startled to see me looking in at them on the second floor of the bus, though today it is only a one-story bus, nearly empty but for some retirees, and I read a book about growing up in India, and think how appropriate it is to read this book on the Number Five bus, bound uptown, not past Union Square and the statue of Gandhi, but the Fireman's Memorial at 100th Street, the promenade of joggers and nodding junkies, nannies with babies and mothers with babies, and old men smelling the forsythia and observing the iris and the gilded phalloi of the croci, not pronounced with a hard "c" as I always said, but with a "sh," sibilant like the breeze itself, and I have my teenage daughter to thank for that bit of information, and I hope she is well, crosstown, at school, studying math or physics, because I am well on Riverside Drive, caught in a reverie of the park and the buildings and the people of the Upper West Side, and the slow ascent of the Number Five bus up the Drive, and the sun out, sky blue like it hasn't been for weeks, and the temperature threatening the seventies for the first time this year, though it's always springtime on the Number Five bus, and it's always sunny outside.

THAT JAZZ

Where Duke Ellington Boulevard joins Amsterdam and
Columbus a block and a half off Broadway, I crossed the
street near the Jewish Home for the Aging, street filled with
colorful plastic caps (red, yellow, blue, green) from crack vials,
and amid the bark of chihuahuas, the growl of pit dogs, the
low moan of alley cats in heat, and the hum of electricity from
a broken neon sign over the bodega, I heard a mother yell,
"Oye, Papo, don't forget the dinero," and then I saw it, this
moment of pure jazz, the Pleasant Avenue bus driver singing
"Autumn Leaves" at the top of his lungs off key, passionately,
out the little window next to his driver's seat, the light
switching from green to orange to red, and an old Dominican
man on a stoop rattling dice in his ancient hands as a small
boy announces 443, he says, 443, the numbers for the day at
four o'clock in the afternoon, teatime for an English professor
at Columbia who flirts with a young woman from Long Island
but who was born in Pusan, Korea, and who wants to write a
long poem about pomegranates, and, just then, at 4:01 p.m.,
jazz everywhere on Duke Ellington Boulevard, a single shot
echoes off the beat up old walls of the Castle Hotel's transient
single-room-occupancy bricks, and pigeons explode into the
air from the abandoned old building across from Central Park
that looks like a 19th-century castle, and just then a bunch of
boys and girls in Catholic school uniforms burst across the
street and a gypsy cab screeches to a halt as the biggest dealer
in Manhattan Valley gets out of a fire-engine red BMW four-
door sedan, falling to the ground with a bullet through his
left eye, and the sun goes down long and slow in New Jersey,
bringing night and new music, a deep bass line, piano keys,
leaves falling in the dark, the drug dealer falling to the ground,

blood everywhere, congas, people noise and EMS sirens, cop car sirens, the Sirens of Manhattan Valley, those chthonic spirits of the city's hearth, low-moaning like twenty-five-buck hookers, like dime-store lovers, like paddleball champions after kissing their best friend's sister, like the sister of a great baseball player kissing the hard neck of a Harlem desperado on the break-out from Rikers Island, like the perpetual hum coming from the subway trains below and the planets above, the music of the spheres, the hum of Thelonious Sphere Monk's rhythmneeking, the long low moan of love in the backroom of a tenement on a loveless street two blocks over, like music in the night or simply like life itself, all energy and heat, vector and curve, balls of sweat and lumps of fur, swelling and release, like the light on the bus that simply says Pleasant Avenue, though everyone knows it is really Duke Ellington Boulevard, and night is only moments away when the bus turns and heads across town and up into Harlem, and the rattle of garbage cans mingles with the sacred hush of evening, pigeons billing, starlings sing from the ailanthus trees, sparrows settle on the window sills, and someone dances down the street as if in a night club, not this street of busted dreams, this street of infinite possibility, street of cause and effect, or just a street with no rhyme or reason, a street of indifferent calm, of indifferent potential, a street of violent dreams and real-time beauty.

Take, for instance,
that dark-haired woman
with the red-painted lips

and the tight skirt and blouse,
the high-heel click
as she goes from one building to the next,
looking for her boyfriend
whom she suspects is unfaithful,
or that young boy with the slick hair and

the new shoes that are as pointy as knives or even the old
couple stumbling down the block after an afternoon of drinks
and gab in the corner bar, and the off-duty cop who thinks no
one knows he is there in his Chevy four-door sedan of civil-
servant blue with radio antennae everywhere over the trunk.
The world is old tonight,

and it is also quite young, besides the world being dangerous
and as free as the birds in the sky or the gangs of young boys
delivering drugs, but really only mules for the big boys uptown,
or the girls out pretending to be high-fashion models in their
mules.

EXIT PURSUED BY A BEAR

As if on cue, love enters the front room,
A force of nature, with a burning sense
Of justice, long legged and short-waisted,
Beautiful, also an intelligence
Burning behind those piercing eyes, I think
We have met before, but we have not met
Until this moment in the front room in
Which a light seems to pierce everything.

Immediately I try to argue
With this state in which I find myself
Beside you, but that is beside the very point,
The point being that it is you beside
Me, godlike human, companion, partner,
Challenger of all my assumptions, friend.

LESS

Each day there is less to say, each hour goes by, each time I sit to write, or times when I say it aloud, elbow bent, mouth slung open in the form of a terrified *O*, remember the time we did the town, my partner says, but I forget what she is talking about, I am toothless, full of beer and wine, full of it, empty my origin, out here on the park bench, the light fades, the shadows fill with knives and guns, there are three cigarettes left, some almonds in my pocket, a dried apricot, and I hold a paddleball racket in my hand, or I bounce the hard black ball on the concrete, counting 1, 2, 3, 4, and so on, remembering nothing, forgetful of my name, thank God for this old overcoat, tweed, thank goodness it's not going to rain, there are clouds to be sure, red streaks at sundown, park birds (sparrow, swift, pigeon, even doves lately), and your hand in mine, and my other hand holding the paddleball racket, and I hear my wine bottle click against your pocketbook, I hear traffic sounds, nothing to say, nothing to do, I am remembering just that, burnt-off images of my former life, that devilish smile which won your heart, remembering your eyes, less red than now, full of wanton desire and mystery, and me then still full of it, full of swagger, and you with your breasts and me with my testicles, and them with their breasts, and there was more than change in my pocket, I had a future of sorts, I was a kind of professor, you said, I was kind to you, and I was, I was. Did I ever tell you about the time I played Hamlet?

"The rest is silence"

Acknowledgments

Some of these short lyrical prose pieces and prose poems have appeared in *Exquisite Corpse, Poet Lore, Ohio Review, Poetry New York, Instant Classics, The Westsider, The Chelsea Clinton News, Pacific Coast Journal, Witness, Hanging Loose, DeCasp,* and *Up Late: American Poetry Since 1970,* edited by Andrei Codrescu.

About the Author

Born in Washington, D.C., to an Irish father and an American mother, **M. G. Stephens** grew up in Bedford-Stuyvesant, Brooklyn and Long Island in a family of sixteen children. His fiction often portrays the crises of large immigrant families in existential struggles to survive in America. He attended the City University of New York (City College), where he earned his B.A. and M.A. in English and writing, and then attended Yale University, earning an M.F.A. in drama (writing, theatre history, and dramatic literature). Many years later he earned a Ph.D. in literature and American studies from the University of Essex in Colchester, England. He wrote his thesis—the British doctoral study—on the origins of the St. Mark's Church in the Bowery's Poetry Project.

He has published many works of short lyrical prose, including *Paragraphs, Still Life, Shipping Out, Circles End,* and *Jigs and Reels.* His first book of poetry, *Alcohol Poems,* came out in 1973, followed by *Tangun Legend* (1978), *Translations,* from Korean (1984), *After Asia* (1993), and more recently *Occam's Razor* (2015) and *Top Boy* (2017). These books have been praised by poets and fiction writers as diverse as Seamus Heaney, Gilbert Sorrentino, William Arrowsmith, Hubert Selby, Jr. and Maureen Howard. He is also the author of the acclaimed novels *The Brooklyn Book of the Dead* and *Season at Coole.* He has published several nonfiction works, including the travel memoir *Lost in Seoul* (1990) and the memoir *Where the Sky Ends* (1999); and such essay collections as *The Dramaturgy of Style* and *Green Dreams* (1994), winner of the AWP award for creative nonfiction.

History of Theatre or the Glass of Fashion grew out of his interests in theatre history, an obsession with Hamlet, and his lifelong passion for the prose poem.